Max Smart

and the

PERILOUS PELLETS

MAX SMART
and the
PERILOUS PELLETS

**KAOS AND CONTROL BOTH HAVE THE
MEANS TO DESTROY EACH OTHER—
SO BOTH ORGANIZATIONS ARE IN
DANGER OF BEING DESTROYED.**

It looked like an ordinary green pea, but that tiny
pellet could mean the end of KAOS—and it was
up to Max Smart to see that Control planted its
explosives before the KAOS agents planted theirs.

In an atom-powered helicopter, piloted by Lance Chalfont, silent birdman (courageous, compassionate and
conscientious, but unable to read a map), Max and
Agent 99 set off on their vital mission, carrying the
satchel of explosives that determined the future of the
world—and their jobs.

The first stop was the scientific laboratory in the middle
of the Sahara Desert, run by the nefarious Dr. Yeh!;
then the Weapons Arsenal deep under the Atlantic
where Dr. Gill, half man, half fish, could apprehend
them and use his deadly weapon; next was the training
school high in the Alps, presided over by The Professor,
a man whose ideas were old-fashioned but fatally effective; then, the building that masqueraded as an Old
Agents Home—what dreadful devices were behind those
walls?

Racing neck and neck to the secret Control sites were
the KAOS men, and all of Max's remarkable talent and
ingenuity are called into play in his most perilous adventure.

You will find the same absorbing reading and high quality in other TEMPO BOOKS. Look for them wherever books are sold. If your dealer does not have the TEMPO BOOKS you want, you may order them by mail, enclosing the list price plus 10¢ a copy to cover mailing.

A complete list of titles is available free from TEMPO BOOKS, Grosset & Dunlap, Inc., 51 Madison Avenue, New York, New York 10010; some of the books you will enjoy are listed in the back of this book.

Max Smart
and the
PERILOUS PELLETS

by

WILLIAM JOHNSTON

A TEMPO BOOKS *Original*

BOOKS

GROSSET & DUNLAP

NEW YORK

A TEMPO BOOKS *Original*

TEMPO BOOKS EDITION, 1966
FIRST PRINTING, SEPTEMBER 1966

Max Smart

and the

PERILOUS PELLETS

1.

MAX SMART, otherwise known as Agent 86 of Control, stepped from his car, glanced to the left, then to the right, then strode forward toward the secret entrance to Control Headquarters. Max should have also looked to the front. For the moment he strode forward he tripped over a small boy and fell flat on his face.

"Shine, mister?" the small boy asked. Having lowered Max to his level, he was now eye-to-eye with him.

"I don't have time for a shine, sonny," Max replied, rising. "You see, I just received an emergency call from the Chief. Something big is popping. The fate of the entire civilized world is probably hanging in the balance again."

The small boy looked at him disappointedly. "You shouldn't make up stories, mister," he said. "It'll become a habit. When you grow up, no one will believe anything you say. Remember the boy who cried 'Wolf!'?"

Max frowned, shaking his head. "No—what about the boy who cried 'Wolf!'?"

The boy placed his shoe shine box in front of Max.

"Put your foot right there and I'll tell you about it," he said.

Max placed a foot on the box. "Yes . . . ?"

"Well, once upon a time," the small boy began, smearing polish on Max's shoe, "there was a little boy named Pedro Hernandez. He lived in a small town called Andy's Mountain. Pedro's father ran the local coffee house."

"Coffee house?"

"A small café that served only coffee," the small boy explained. "The men of the town would sit in the coffee house drinking coffee from morn 'til night. There was one man, however, who was no longer allowed to sit in the coffee house and drink coffee from morn 'til night. His name was Wolf Barnschlager. And the reason Wolf Barnschlager was not allowed to sit in the coffee house and drink coffee from morn 'til night was because for years Wolf Barnschlager had been sitting in the coffee house drinking coffee from morn 'til night and he had run up a tab of four-hundred-and-seven dollars and twenty-eight cents, including tax."

"I see. A deadbeat."

"No, he was still very much alive," the small boy replied, buffing Max's shoe. "In fact, a rumor began circulating in Andy's Mountain that Wolf Barnschlager planned to disguise himself as a local Indian named Francis X. Sheepfoot, enter the coffee house, order a cup of coffee, drink it, then slip out without paying for it, thereby executing a cruel but clever hoax."

Max sighed sadly. "Everybody picks on the Indians."

"Yes. Well, soon after that, little Pedro observed a man entering the coffee house who looked suspiciously like Francis X. Sheepfoot. Immediately, so as to alert his father, he cried, 'Wolf! Wolf!' His father, alerted, rushed at the man, got him by the feathers, and hurled him bodily from the coffee house."

"I know," Max smiled. "But, as it turned out, the

man who looked suspiciously like Francis X. Sheepfoot was, in fact, not Wolf Barnschlager, but Francis X. Sheepfoot. Right?"

"No, it was Wolf Barnschlager, all right," the small boy replied. "Other shoe, please."

Max placed the other shoe on the shine box. "Then why was it wrong for Pedro to cry 'Wolf! Wolf!'?" he asked.

"Wrong? It wasn't wrong. It was exactly the right thing to do. His father rewarded him handsomely. He made him assistant manager of the coffee house."

Max looked down at the boy puzzledly. "Then I don't see the point—"

He was interrupted by a ringing sound.

"Excuse me," Max said. "I'll have to have my shoe back. It's ringing."

The small boy groaned. "It happens every time! Right in the middle of a shine!"

Max removed his foot from the box, then removed the shoe from his foot.

Max: Maxwell Smart, Secret Agent 86 here.

Chief: Max! Where are you? We're waiting!

Max: I'm on my way, Chief. I'm right outside Headquarters now. The instant this boy finishes polishing my telephone, I'll be right in.

Operator: Polishing your telephone! If that boy ruins our instrument, there'll be Bell to pay!

Chief: Max, this is no time to get a shoe shine!

Max: Same old thing hanging in the balance again, Chief?

Chief: Worse, Max! Worse—believe me! Now, get in here!

Operator: The idea! Smearing gunk all over our phone!

Max: Please accept my apology—both of you. I'm on my way, Chief.

Max slipped his shoe back on his foot. "I'm sorry I can't stay to hear the end of the story," he said to the small boy.

"That *was* the end," the boy replied. "Unless, of course, you're interested in the part about—" He shook his head. "No, you wouldn't be interested in that part."

"I would, I would," Max said. "What happened?"

"That's Part II," the boy replied. "You get Part II when you get a second shoe shine."

"Drat!" Max said. "Just when it was getting interesting, too. Look, uh, would it be in bad taste to get my second shoe shine right now? I know you shoe shine boys have your rules and all that, but—"

Max's shoe began ringing again.

"The Chief again," Max said. "I better get inside." He handed the small boy a coin. "Anyway," he said, "thank you for a very enjoyable experience." He patted the boy's head. "You're a bright lad, and I'm sure you'll go far."

The boy picked up his box. "It's not in the cards," he said sorrowfully.

"Oh?"

"I'm failure-prone," the boy replied. "Look at me now—a lowly shoe shine boy. And—would you believe it?—I was once the assistant manager of a coffee house."

"You mean . . . ?"

"If you ever need another shine, look me up," the boy said, walking away. "Ask for Pedro."

Max stared after him for a moment, then turned and entered Control Headquarters. "I'd *still* like to hear the details," he said to himself.

When Max reached the Chief's office he rapped briskly on the door.

"How many 's's in Mississippi?" a voice responded.

"I don't know, Chief—how many 's's are there in Mississippi?" Max asked.

"Max, that's the code for today!"

"Oh. Well, let's see, there are four 'a's in Alabama. And there are two 'l's in Pennsyllvania. And there are—"

"Max! The correct answer is, 'there are no "s"s in Mississippi!' "

"I don't think that's quite right, Chief. I may not be too great on Pennsylvania, but I'm a whiz on Mississippi. There happen to be—"

"Max! Come in!"

Max opened the door and stepped into the Chief's office. He saw Agent 99 seated in a chair next to the desk. "99," he said, "would you straighten the Chief out on Mississippi? He seems to think—"

"Max, he was using the code," 99 replied. "The code is, 'There are no "s"s in Mississippi.' In other words, the wrong answer is the right answer. But, if you didn't know the code, you wouldn't know that. So, you'd give the right answer—and that would be the wrong answer. You couldn't get in here without the wrong answer, Max."

"I see. Then how did I get in here?"

"In your case, I always make an exception, Max," the Chief explained. "You never have the wrong answer."

Max smiled appreciatively. "Thank you, Chief."

"You're welcome. Now, can we get down to business?"

Max put up a hand. "Just a minute, Chief. I haven't punched in." He went to the rack of time cards, selected one, then placed it into the slot of the time clock. A bell rang. Max extracted the card and placed it back in the rack. "Which reminds me," Max said, turning back to the Chief. "My last pay check was short a dollar and seventy-four cents."

"Well, I'm sorry, Max, but—"

"For overtime," Max said, approaching the desk. "I don't want to be petty about it, but if I owed Control a dollar and seventy-four cents for overtime, I would certainly pay up. What's sauce for the goose is sauce for the gander."

"I'll try to—"

"It isn't much, I know, if you think of it in dollars and cents," Max said. "But translate it into marbles, at three for a penny, and it would come to quite a handful."

"I know, Max, I know," the Chief said. "I'll send a note to Accounting and make sure that you get your money."

"Ahhhh, Chief . . . could I have it in marbles? It will seem like a lot more."

"Anything you say, Max," the Chief sighed. "Now, may we discuss the case at hand?"

Max seated himself in the chair at the other side of the Chief's desk. "I wondered when you were going to get around to that," he said. "You seemed pretty excited when you interrupted my shoe shine."

"Max," the Chief said, leaning forward, "this is the most important case you've ever been handed."

"You mean the fate of the entire civilized world is hanging in the balance again, eh?"

"It's even more drastic than that. Max, this time it's the fate of Control that's hanging in the balance."

"You know what that means, Max," 99 said.

"Right! Our jobs are at stake!" He faced back to the Chief. "Give it to me straight, Chief."

"All right, Max, here it is. Control has acquired possession of KAOS's 'Little Black Book.' That book contains data on the location, layout and organizational structure of every one of KAOS's installations."

"Good for us," Max smiled. "How did we do that, Chief?"

"One of the KAOS agents left it lying on a lunch counter," the Chief replied. "And, by a stroke of luck, the waitress who was serving him was one of *our* agents.

But that's not all, Max. Just as we acquired possession of KAOS's Little Black Book, our Research and Development Department completed work on a compact and especially destructive explosive. This explosive is very tiny. It's about the size—" He reached into his pocket. "Here, I'll show you," he said, holding out a tiny green pellet the size of a pea.

"Chief, I think I can tell you what you had for dinner the last time you wore that suit," Max said.

"No, Max, this is it. This is the explosive. As you can see, it's no larger than a pea."

"Amazing!" Max said, taking the pellet from the Chief and holding it up. "It actually looks like a pea. I wonder how it would taste with roast beef?"

"Don't try it," the Chief warned, retrieving the pellet and putting it back into his pocket. "Now, Max, the important thing about this explosive is that it can be planted at one time and detonated any time later, and from somewhere else. In fact, from *any*where else."

"I see. It has a long fuse, right?"

"No, Max. This explosive is electronically operated." He pointed to a button on his desk. "If I were to punch this button, Max, every pellet, everywhere, would explode. This is the electronic control. Do you realize, Max, what would happen if I punched that button?"

Max nodded. "It would rain peas."

"Not quite, Max. Try again."

"Well, let's see. There is a pea in your pocket. So that means that you would probably ruin a perfectly good suit."

"You're getting closer, Max. Let's just suppose that one of these explosives had been planted in each of the KAOS installations. Then, let's just suppose that I punched this button. Can you visualize the result?"

Max closed his eyes tightly. "Yes . . . I can see it. It looks like an early Fourth of July."

"Exactly, Max," the Chief said.

"Chief, how are Max and I involved in this?" 99 asked.

"Your mission, 99—and Max—is to travel to each of the KAOS installations, infiltrate, and plant an explosive. After you have done that, you are to return to Headquarters."

"I see," 99 said. "And then—"

The Chief nodded. "And then, I will punch the button."

"Chief, isn't that a little silly?" Max said. "After we've gone to all the trouble of planting those peas, then you're going to blow them up?"

"And blow up the KAOS installations, too, Max," the Chief explained.

"Oh, yes . . . I see. Very clever, Chief. I never would have thought of that."

"That's wonderful, Chief!" 99 enthused. "We now have the means to destroy KAOS completely for once and all!"

"Exactly," the Chief smiled.

"Ahhh . . . one thing," Max said. "Chief, when you opened this discussion, you told us that the fate of Control was hanging in the balance. But, the way it sounds to me, it's the fate of KAOS that's hanging in the balance."

"That's very observant of you, Max," the Chief replied. "As a matter of fact, there's more to the story."

"I see. Part II, eh?"

"You might say that, yes."

Max put his foot up on the Chief's desk. "I suppose you'll want to shine my shoe while you tell it."

The Chief pushed the shoe aside. "No, I don't believe so. But I understand what you mean. I do business with Pedro, too."

"What is Part II, Chief?" 99 asked.

"Well, as you know, Control has—or, rather, *had*— a 'Little Black Book' that is similar—or, rather, identical

—to KAOS's Little Black Book. Unfortunately, one of our agents left it on a lunch counter. And, doubly unfortunately, the waitress was a KAOS agent."

Max pounded a hand against the side of his head. "I think there's an echo in here, Chief," he said. "I'm hearing things twice."

"No, it's a different story, it just sounds the same," the Chief said. "And, to make it even more of a coincidence, we have been informed by one of our informers at KAOS that KAOS's Research and Development Department has developed a compact and especially destructive explosive that can be planted at one time and detonated any time later and from afar."

"There goes that echo again, Chief," Max complained.

"Chief," 99 said, "could it be that at this very moment—"

"Yes," the Chief broke in. "At this very moment, a KAOS agent is attempting to infiltrate our installations and plant the KAOS explosives. And when and if he completes the mission he is to return to KAOS Headquarters. At that time, KAOS will—" The Chief shuddered.

"Yes, yes, what?" Max asked.

"Let me put it this way . . . on the desk of the Chief at KAOS there is a button. . . ."

Max pounded the side of his head again. "Chief, I'm *sure* there's an echo in here."

"Then it's a race, is that it, Chief?" 99 said.

"Exactly, 99. You and Max will be attempting to plant explosives in the KAOS installations. And, at the same time, the KAOS agent will be attempting to plant explosives in the Control installations. The winner will be the winner. We're calling this: Operation Button Button Who'll Punch the Button!"

"If I've doped this out correctly," Max said, rising, "we don't have a second to lose. Every wasted moment puts Control in more and more danger. 99—let's go!"

Max strode to the door, whipped it open, charged from the room, and dashed down the corridor.

The Chief shook his head woefully.

99 rolled her eyes ceilingward.

Together and in silence they waited.

A few moments later, Max reappeared in the doorway. "99—you're not with me," he said chastisingly.

"Max—"

"99, there's no more time for idle chatter! That KAOS agent is out there somewhere attempting to infiltrate our installations. We should be doing the same thing."

"Max—think," the Chief said. "Where is it you'll be going?"

"To infiltrate our installations."

"Where, Max . . . ?"

"I just told you. To infil—" Max frowned, thinking. "Oh, yes, I see what you mean. Apparently, Chief, I got Part I and Part II a little mixed up. And no wonder —with that echo in here. Let's see now, it isn't *our* installations we're to infiltrate, it's *their* installations— right?"

"Right, Max!"

"Got it!" Max said. "Let's go, 99!" Again, he charged from the room and dashed down the corridor.

The Chief covered his eyes with a hand and leaned his elbow on his desk.

99 made soft humming sounds.

Together they waited.

A few minutes later, Max returned. He entered the office, looking slightly crestfallen, and sat down again in the chair beside the Chief's desk.

"I hate to be picky, Chief," Max said, "but you forgot to tell us where the KAOS installations are located."

"I'm glad you *thought* of that, Max," the Chief said.

"I'm nothing if not thorough," Max replied.

The Chief picked up a black satchel that was beside

his chair and put it on the desk. "All the information you'll need is in here," he said. "I've had a 'fact sheet' prepared on each of the KAOS installations. It gives the location and a little background on the KAOS man in charge. I think you'll find the information interesting, and I hope that, as well, you'll find it helpful." He opened the black satchel and got out a small plastic bag. It appeared to contain peas. "These pellets are the explosives," he said. "Your task will be to plant one pellet at each installation."

"There are a *lot* of peas there, Chief," Max said. "Are there that many KAOS installations?"

The Chief shook his head. "No, Max. But I thought you'd better have an extra-large supply. I know how you misplace things."

"Chief, that's unfair. What did I ever lose?"

"Remember? On your last case? When the Navy loaned you the aircraft carrier 'Lexington'?"

"Chief, the 'Lexington' is *not* lost. I still say it will turn up somewhere."

"Until it does, Max, I think we'd better play it safe. Take *all* of these pellets with you."

"What are those other things in the satchel, Chief?" 99 asked, peering over the Chief's shoulder.

"Oh . . . these. These are some gadgets cooked up by Research & Development," the Chief replied. "I'm not sure what they are, but the instructions are printed on the labels. They might come in handy." He closed the satchel and handed it to Max. "Here you are. Guard this with your life."

"Won't I be taking a chance, carrying this little black bag?" Max said, accepting the satchel. "Someone is liable to mistake me for a doctor."

"What harm would that do?"

"Suppose this someone asked me to take out an appendix?"

"Just explain that you don't have time."

"Chief! I couldn't do that. When I received my medical degree, I swore an oath. Through rain, through snow, through dark of night, I swore to heal the sick and deliver the mail."

"Max, number one, you have your oaths confused. And, number two, carrying a little black bag does not make you a doctor."

"Sorry, Chief. I guess I got a little carried away."

"And that's what you're going to get again," the Chief said. "Right now, standing by at the airport, there is a helicopter waiting to carry you away. The helicopter will transport you to each of the KAOS installations."

"A helicopter, Chief?" 99 said puzzledly. "Are the KAOS installations that close together?"

"No, they're in widely separated parts of the world," the Chief replied.

"But . . . doesn't a helicopter have a limited range?" 99 said.

"Yes, normally, but—"

"99, I'm surprised," Max broke in. "Isn't it obvious? This helicopter can be refueled in mid-air. All around the globe there are refueling planes waiting to gas us up when we start running low. It's exactly the way I would have planned it if I'd been planning it."

"That isn't exactly it, Max," the Chief said. "You see—"

"Of course I see, Chief," Max interrupted. "This is an electric helicopter, right? It doesn't need fuel."

"Max—an electric helicopter?" 99 said. "But how would—"

"Simple," Max replied, anticipating the question. "A very, very, very, very, very *long* cord."

"No, Max," the Chief said, shaking his head. "You're still not right. This is an atom-powered helicopter. It doesn't use conventional fuel. It can stay aloft almost forever, barring any mechanical malfunctions, of course."

Max smiled. "That's a little difficult to believe, Chief."

"Well, you'll find out when you get to the airport."

Max looked hurt. "Chief, I said, 'That's a little difficult to believe, Chief.' "

"Oh, all right, Max. Then, would you believe that it's steam-powered and the pilot carries an extra tea kettle?"

"I don't think so," Max replied dubiously.

"Then would you believe that it's water-powered and operates only over waterfalls?"

"That's a *lit-tle* closer to it," Max replied. "But, if you don't mind, Chief, I'll wait 'til I get to the airport and get a closer look at it before I decide whether or not you're telling the truth. You won't be offended, will you?"

"Not unless I'm subjected to more of this idiotic conversation," the Chief replied. "Max, will you get going! The fate of Control is hanging in the balance!"

"Chief, I'm on my way," Max said. "With Max Smart on the job, Control has nothing to fear."

Max charged across the room, out the doorway, and down the corridor.

The Chief slumped into his chair.

99 inspected her fingernails.

A moment later, Max reappeared.

"Forget something, Max?" the Chief asked.

"Yes, as a matter of fact—"

"Here," the Chief said, rising and handing him the black satchel.

"Oh, yes, I guess I forgot about that, too," Max said accepting the bag.

"Was there something—or some*one*—else, Max?" 99 smiled, joining him.

"Come to think of it, I *did* forget you, didn't I?" Max said.

"You mean there's still something *else* you forgot?" the Chief asked.

"Yes. That's why I came back," Max replied. "I wanted to remind you, Chief. You better do something about that echo in here. Some day, at some crucial moment, it's liable to cause some confusion."

"I'll take care of it, Max," the Chief sighed, slumping back into his chair.

2.

Max and 99 hurried from Control headquarters, then, in Max's car, raced to the airport. Reaching there, they drove to Control's private hangar, where, on the apron, the atom-powered helicopter was warming up. The noise of the engine and rotors was deafening.

"Here we are!" Max yelled to 99 over the roar.

"Why would I want a cigar?" 99 hollered back puzzledly.

"You're right, it wasn't very far," Max replied, getting out of the car.

They hurried across the apron to the helicopter. The pilot was in the cockpit, leaning out the window.

"We're from Control!" Max bellowed up to him.

"Who's standing in a hole?" the pilot yelled.

Max turned to 99. "He says to get aboard and bring the pole!" he hollered.

99 cupped a hand to her ear. "Stroll where?"

Max shook his head, indicating that he could not hear. Then he and 99 got aboard the helicopter and made their way to the cockpit.

The pilot was a handsome, blond, granite-jawed, steely-eyed young man. He nodded to them perfunctorily.

"We're all set!" Max shouted.

The pilot shook his head. "I don't bet!" he yelled back.

Max reached forward and closed the cockpit window, shutting out most of the engine racket. "Now then," he said, "what pole was it that you wanted us to bring aboard?"

"Pole?" the pilot replied. "I thought you said hole."

"I thought he said cigar," 99 put in.

"Maybe we'd better start all over," Max suggested. He extended a hand. "I'm Max Smart, Agent 86," he said. "And this," he added, nodding toward 99, "is 99, Agent 99."

The pilot took the hand. "Lance Chalfont, silent birdman, here," he said. "I don't talk much about myself—that's why they call me a silent birdman. The way I figure it, if a man is courageous, compassionate and conscientious, he doesn't have to talk about it—folks'll notice it. You'll see. As the hours pass, and you get to admire me more and more, you'll see that it won't be because of anything I say, it'll be because of what I do. Actions speak louder than words. You'll wonder to yourself, you'll wonder, 'I wonder if Lance'd tell me about some of his hair-raisin' adventures?' But you won't get a word out of me. Like that time I saved them pygmies from themselves. Want to hear that?"

Max shook his head. "No, I think we'd better get going."

"Good thing you don't want to hear about it," Lance Chalfont said. " 'Cause you'd never get a thing out of me. The way it happened was, you see, I'd crash landed in this jungle. Well, no sooner'd I crawled out of the wreckage than here comes these pygmies. 'My Heaven!

school must be out!' I said to myself. A bunch of itty-
bitty fellas, they was. No taller'n a second-grader that'd
been brought up standin' under a porch! And, the next
thing I knowed, they started throwin' spears at me.
Didn't hit me, of course. A man like me, courageous,
compassionate and conscientious, can't be hit. 'Here,
now!' I said to them pygmies. 'Is that any way to
behave?' Well, that caught 'em like a whack across the
backside with a canoe paddle. They come in closer and
started lookin' me over. So I addressed them. 'Boys,' I
said, 'just look at yourselves! Runnin' around the jungle
like that! Throwin' spears! You oughta be ashamed of
yourselves.' Then, lookin' down on 'em from my
towerin' height, I said, 'Boys! Grow up!' "

"Yes, well that's very interesting," Max said. "But
now, could we—"

"Did 'em a world of good," Lance Chalfont continued. "It was just what they needed—a good talkin'
to. And—you know?—today, them pygmies is six feet
tall."

"That *is* interesting," Max said. "However—"

"You won't get any stories like that out of me,
though," Lance Chalfont said. "The one thing a silent
birdman won't do, he won't boast. Though, shucks
knows, this one here's certainly got reason to. You'll
look a fur distance before you find anybody as courageous, compassionate and conscientious as Lance Chalfont. Not that I'd say that myself. I'm just quotin' what
everybody else that knows me says."

"Could we leave now?" Max said wearily.

"You wanta go? Shoulda said something. In this
world, son, you gotta blow your own horn. If you don't,
nobody'll blow it for you." He smiled sweetly. "Where
we goin'?"

"Oh, yes, that—" Max said. He opened the black
satchel and got out a sheaf of official orders. "Ah . . .

let's see . . . Our first destination is KAOS's Science Laboratory, and it's located in . . . the Sahara Desert?"

"Know the place well," Lance Chalfont said, revving up the engine. "I got a story about the Sahara Desert I could tell if I wasn't a silent birdman. The way it goes is . . ."

The engine roared, drowning out Lance Chalfont's words, and the helicopter rose from the ground and then, high aloft, swung east. Soon they were winging swiftly across the ocean.

"Hadn't we better look at the fact sheet on the installation, Max?" 99 said. "We'll want to know all we can about it before we try to infiltrate."

"Excellent idea," Max said, getting a second sheaf of papers from the black satchel. He studied the first page. "That's odd," he said. "This fact sheet says the installation is six fathoms below sea level. In the Sahara Desert? I didn't think the KAOS people were that clever."

"Max," 99 said, looking over his shoulder, "you have the wrong fact sheet. That's the fact sheet for KAOS's weapons arsenal under the Atlantic Ocean."

"Oh . . . yes." Max got out another fact sheet. "Here it is," he said. He shook the sheaf of papers. "Little sand in it," he explained. "According to this," he continued, reading, "the KAOS science lab is commanded by the infamous Dr. Yeh! Oh-oh!"

"What is it, Max?"

"Well, apparently the infamous Dr. Yeh! has been stationed in the desert too long. He thinks he's a sheik. And he runs the KAOS science lab like a sheikdom."

"Sahara Desert below!" Lance Chalfont called out.

Max and 99 looked out the window.

"But that's water down there," Max said.

Lance Chalfont frowned. "Accordin' to my calculatin', that's the Sahara Desert," he insisted.

"Look for yourself," Max challenged.

Lance Chalfont peered out his window. "That sure is

wet sand, ain't it!" he said. "A fella'd have trouble, all right, keepin' it inside a sandbox."

"Let's keep going for a while," Max suggested. "When you see some dry sand, sing out again." He turned back to 99. "We better think up a story," he said. "Something logical. If we show up in the middle of the Sahara Desert claiming that we took a wrong turn in Altoona, Pennsylvania, the KAOS people are liable to be a little suspicious. Now, think, 99, what can we use for an excuse?"

"Tell 'em you're a couple secret agents," Lance Chalfont said. "In the long run, honesty's the best policy. When you lie, boy, speak right out, tell the truth. People'll respect you for it."

Max ignored him. "We could claim to be camel-herders," he said to 99. "We could say that we've lost our herd."

"Very good, Max," 99 said. "It's logical, at least."

"Then that's it," Max said. "We'll—"

"Thar she blows!" Lance Chalfont bellowed.

"What blows?" Max asked.

"The sand! See it down there? Blowin' all over the place!"

Max and 99 looked out again. "Yes, that's it, all right," Max said. He reached into the black satchel, got out a map, and handed it to Lance Chalfont. "This will give you the exact latitude and longitude of the KAOS science lab," he said.

Lance Chalfont tossed the map back to him. "Can't read them things," he said. "They got lines drawed all over 'em. Every time I look for a place I want to go, it's got a line drawed through it."

"Then how do you find your way?" Max asked him acidly.

"Usually, I just stop at a fillin' station and ask," Lance Chalfont replied. He pointed. "There's a fillin' station up ahead. We'll stop there."

Max raised up and looked out the front window. "That's an oasis," he corrected.

"Call it anything you want," Lance Chalfont replied. "To me, it's a foreign fillin' station."

Lance Chalfont landed the helicopter near the oasis, then got out and walked to the well, where an Arab was watering his camel. He spoke with the Arab, then returned to the helicopter.

"What did he say?" Max asked, as the helicopter rose into the air.

"It's just over that next hill," Lance Chalfont replied.

"Dune," Max said.

"I'm doin' the best I can. Don't rattle me with all that yammerin'. Know why I'm called a silent birdman? 'Cause when I'm zeroin' in on my destination, I want a lot of silence from you birds!"

"Yes. Well, we'll—"

"There she is!" Lance Chalfont pointed.

Max and 99 looked out the front window. They saw an enclave of cement buildings surrounded by a high cement wall.

"Land behind one of those dunes—uh, hills—and we'll approach the installation on foot," Max said. "A couple camelherders flying around in an atom-powered helicopter might be just a wee bit much. Undoubtedly, it would cast some doubt on our story."

"Max, you think of everything," 99 smiled.

"It's the little things that count," Max said.

Lance Chalfont landed the helicopter behind a dune, and Max and 99 got out. "Wait here," Max commanded.

"Better shake a leg," Lance Chalfont said. "I'm gonna keep the meter runnin'." He grinned. "That's a silent birdman joke, boy."

Max nodded. "Very funny." Then he and 99 set out across the sand.

When they reached the top of the dune, they halted. "I wish we had a pair of binoculars," Max said. "I'd like to get a look at that installation before we approach it."

"Try the black bag, Max," 99 suggested.

Max raised the black bag to his eyes. "Nope. Can't see a thing."

"I mean look inside the black bag. Maybe R & D sent some binoculars."

"Oh . . . yes." Max opened the satchel. "Ah, here we are—a pair of binoculars. Good old R & D!" He put the binoculars to his eyes. "That's odd," he said, "I can't see a thing." He lowered the binoculars.

"Max," 99 said, "you have two black, sooty rings around your eyes."

He dropped the binoculars back into the satchel. "R & D is having its little joke again," he said disgustedly. "If there's anything more useless than an R & D department with a sense of humor, I don't know what it is!" He bent down to the satchel again. "Wait a minute—what's this?" When he straightened, he was holding a foot-long aluminum rod. "Collapsible pole for vaulting over high walls," he said, reading the label on the rod. "Good old R & D!"

"Then we won't have to pose as camelherders," 99 said.

"Exactly. We'll use this pole, vault over the wall, and land on the inside."

Crouching low, Max and 99 approached the wall. When they got nearer they saw that the wall was patrolled by guards.

"This will call for perfect timing," Max said. "If you'll notice, 99, you'll see that there is a period of about three seconds when all of the guards are out of sight. That's KAOS's one mistake. In that three seconds, we will gallop toward the wall, vault, and disappear inside."

"I'm ready, Max."

"This will be tricky," Max said. "It will be a twovaulter vault. In other words, we'll both have to vault at the same time, using the one pole. And, in addition, one of us will have to carry the black satchel."

"We can do it, Max," 99 said stoutly.

"All right—ready? There go the guards. They're out of sight! Let's go, 99!"

Holding the pole between them, Max and 99 raced across the sand toward the wall. In addition, Max was carrying the black bag.

"Now!" Max cried.

They plunged the end of the pole into the sand and rose up, up, up, up—then, slowly, down, down, down.

"I think there's been a slight miscalculation," Max said.

"Yes," 99 nodded. "The pole is sinking into the sand. And we're still outside the wall."

"Well, we'll be *in*side very soon," Max assured her. "Here come the guards."

As the pole sank further and further into the sand, the guards gathered at the base, waiting for Max and 99 to reach the ground. They shouted, in a language that neither Max nor 99 could understand.

"That explains something that's been puzzling me," Max said. "I wondered why they were dressed like Arabs. Now I know."

"They *are* Arabs, Max."

"Yes, that's what I've decided, too."

When Max and 99 had descended to within a few feet of the ground, the guards grabbed them and hustled them inside the wall. They were taken to a large building, then into a huge auditorium-size room. The room was richly decorated. A thick red carpet stretched from the entrance to the far side. It ended at a large, jewel-encrusted throne. And seated on the throne was a plump, apple-cheeked man who was dressed in a white burnoose. The guards prodded Max and 99 toward the throne.

"Ah! Here you are—at last!" the apple-cheeked man greeted them happily.

"Yes, well, we would have been here sooner, but we had a slow pole," Max replied.

One of the guards spoke up, but the apple-cheeked man silenced him. "Don't babble at me!" he scolded. "I don't have to be told who these two are." He smiled at Max. "You are my American Advisor, right? You have been sent to me by the U.S. State Department—is that not correct."

Max nodded. "Yes, that *is* not correct. Let me intro—"

But the apple-cheeked man had turned his attention to 99. "And you," he said, "you are my new dancer."

"I am?" 99 smiled weakly.

"You have come just in time," the apple-cheeked man said to her. "For weeks, my ballet company has not had a flung."

"A flung?" Max asked puzzledly.

"Yes, a flung. You are familiar with ballet, aren't you? Have you not seen the dancers when they lift one of their number from the stage and fling her high into the air? Well, those who do the flinging are the flingers. And the one who is flung is the—"

"Flung," Max nodded.

"Correct. My troupe has been without a flung for weeks. They've tried to substitute a flinger as a flung. But when a bunch of flingers fling another flinger, it's just not the same. No matter how hard they try to pretend, they know—a flinger is not a flung." He smiled at 99. "That's why I sent to Sears Roebuck for you," he explained. "You look exactly like your picture in the catalog."

Max eyed the apple-cheeked man narrowly. "Unless I miss my guess," he said, "you must be the infamous Dr. Yeh!"

"Yeh! Yeh! And your name is . . . ?"

"Around the State Department, I'm known as Max-well Smart," Max replied.

"Max—the State Department?" 99 said.

Max winked. "That's right, ballet dancer, whatever your name is. I've been sent here by the State Department to plant a— That is, to assist Dr. Yeh! in his efforts to—" He faced back to Dr. Yeh! "—to what?" he asked.

"To develop my sheikdom," Dr. Yeh! replied. "We're behind the times. But, with your advice, and your money, we hope soon to become modern." He leaned forward, smiling, and indicated the black satchel. "That's the money, I assume."

"Don't you want a little advice first?" Max said, hedging.

"Oh, is that the way it's done?" Dr. Yeh! shrugged. "All right, what harm can a little advice do?" He motioned to an attendant. "Take the ballet dancer to the ballet dancer place," he ordered.

"Max!" 99 cried, alarmed.

Max appeared to ignore her. "The ballet dancer place?" he said to Dr. Yeh! "Doesn't it have a name?"

"I can never think of it," Dr. Yeh! sighed.

Max smiled. "Is it by any chance called, 'Go along with the pretense until I get a chance to plant the you-know-what, and I'll contact you at the first opportun-ity'?" he asked.

99 nodded that she had understood.

"No. That's close," Dr. Yeh! replied. "But it's shorter."

Max shrugged. "It was only a guess."

The attendant and 99 departed. When they had gone, Dr. Yeh! said to Max, "Now, let's get that advice bit over with. I want to see what's in the bag."

"Do you mind if we take a little stroll about the premises?" Max said. "I advise better when I'm walk-ing."

"Mmmmm, think on your feet, eh? All right." Dr. Yeh! got up from the throne and, taking the lead, started the stroll. "You might want to suggest that we put up some factories," he said. "That's the first step toward modernization, isn't it?"

"Excellent idea," Max replied, following, carrying the black bag, and looking for a place to plant the explosive. "But there's one hitch." He stopped at a huge, waist-high, earthenware jug. "To manufacture, you need raw materials. Out here in the desert, there's an acute shortage of almost everything." He looked into the jug and saw that it was empty.

"I've thought of that," Dr. Yeh! said, pausing. "My idea is to manufacture sand piles. We have the raw material right here at hand."

"Sand piles?" Max reached into the satchel for a pellet. "Yes, I can see the possibilities. Although, frankly, lately the market has been a little slow for sand piles." He dropped the pellet into the jug.

"Ah, yes, but today it's the packaging that counts," Dr. Yeh! replied. "What I have in mind is shipping the sand piles in jugs like this," he said, putting a hand on the jug that Max had just dropped a pellet into. "People would buy the sand piles just to get the jugs. These jugs are—" He had glanced down while talking. "Somebody dropped a pea in my jug," he said, surprised. He reached into the jug, picked out the pellet, and flicked it away. "The help you get today," he said morosely. "Last week, I found dust on a camel. The servant problem is atrocious."

Max ambled idly in the direction in which the pea had rolled. "I wonder if I could have that pea for a souvenir?" he said. "When I left, the Secretary asked me to bring something back. In fact, whenever I go to a foreign country, he asks me to bring something back. He usually wants a mutual defense treaty. But, in this case, I think he'll settle for a pea."

"Take it," Dr. Yeh! said. "I got a pea patch full of 'em."

Max found the pellet and retrieved it. "How would you like a little advice on weeding a pea patch?" he asked.

"*Then* can we open the bag?"

"Not that quickly," Max replied, as the two continued the stroll. "You see, at the State Department our main job is to give advice. The money part of it is just incidental. If I traveled all this distance and did nothing but give you a wad of money, I'd feel I was doing a sloppy job. You wouldn't want me to have *that* on my conscience, would you?"

Dr. Yeh! groaned. "I asked them to send me a money order. And what do I get? A blabbermouth!"

"Why don't you show me your science lab?" Max suggested. "I have a lot of dandy advice on operating science labs."

"Why not?" Dr. Yeh! replied. He turned down a corridor. "Bring the bag," he said.

At the end of the corridor, they reached a blank wall. Nearby, on a pedestal, was a sculpture of a ballet dancer. Dr. Yeh! lowered one of the dancer's legs, and the wall rose automatically into the ceiling, revealing an opening. They proceeded, moving along another corridor, until finally they emerged from the building and entered a lush garden.

"Magnificent camouflage!" Max said. "It doesn't look one bit like a science lab."

Dr. Yeh! frowned. "It isn't a science lab," he said. "We used the wrong blank wall."

Dr. Yeh! led the way back. When they reached the spot from which they had started, he turned in a different direction. A moment later, they reached a second blank wall. But, tacked onto the wall was a small hand-lettered sign. It said: Temporarily Out of Order.

"Too bad," Dr. Yeh! said. "We'll have to try again tomorrow."

"I had my heart set on it," Max pouted.

"I'll show you to your room," Dr. Yeh! said. "I think you'll find it very interesting. It has a built-in tape recorder. If you don't mind a suggestion, why don't you put your advice on tape? I could listen to it at my leisure, some time when I don't have anything else to do. That way, we wouldn't have to delay the business with the black bag, eh?"

"I'll think about it," Max replied. He had spotted a tall, round, waist-high vase, and he angled toward it. "Say . . . there's an interesting piece of pottery," he said.

"Woolworth," Dr. Yeh! replied.

Max stopped at the vase and circled it, inspecting it admiringly. "Beautiful handwork," he said. He palmed the pellet, then, gripping the edge of the vase, dropped it into it.

The pellet hit the bottom of the vase and clinked.

Dr. Yeh! looked inside. "You dropped your souvenir," he said.

"Thank you for bringing it to my attention," Max replied dryly. He put his arm into the vase and retrieved the explosive.

Dr. Yeh! smiled broadly. "What are friends for? Now, it's your turn to do me a favor."

"Anything," Max said grimly. "Anything within reason, that is."

"Just *show* me the money," Dr. Yeh! said. "Hold on to it for another couple hours or so, if you want to, but at least show it to me."

Max thought for a second. Then, "Just a quick glance," he said.

"That's all I ask."

Max held up the satchel, then quickly opened it and closed it. "What color did you see?" he asked.

"Green!" Dr. Yeh! beamed.

"Now, may I go to my room?" Max said.

"Yes, yes, of course," Dr. Yeh! replied, still grinning.

As they moved on down the corridor, Dr. Yeh! said, "I like it. I like the new style."

"The new style?"

"The new round-style money," Dr. Yeh! said. "You know what it reminds me of?"

"Peas, perhaps?"

"Right."

"Everybody comments on that," Max said.

3.

ALONE, FINALLY, in his room, Max hurriedly scribbled
a note to 99. It said: Will meet you at the ballet dancer
place.

Then, opening his door, he peeked out and looked
up and down the corridor. At the far end he saw a guard.

"Hsssst!" Max hissed.

The guard, an Arab, looked at him speculatively for
a second, then, hefting his rifle, approached.

"You speak English, fella?" Max asked.

"Like a native," the guard smiled. "How about you?"

"Yes, I handle it fairly well," Max replied. "Although,
I have trouble with some of the southern and western
dialects. For instance, in southern New York State there
is a place the natives refer to as Lawn Guylin. I've
never been able to find that on a map."

"That's Brooklynese for Albany," the guard explained.

"Oh, is that it? Well, live and learn."

The guard saluted. "Any time you need any more
help," he said, "I'm just down the hall."

"Uh . . . just a second," Max said, gesturing him

back. "That wasn't exactly what I had in mind. I wonder if you would deliver a message for me? Do you know the new dancer in the ballet troupe? She's quartered in the ballet dancer place. Would you take a message to her?"

"I'm on guard," the guard replied. "I can't leave my post."

"Oh, really? What would happen if you got caught?"

"I'd get a red star," the guard replied. "Gold stars are for staying at your post, and red stars are for leaving your post."

"Look, how about this?" Max said. "I'll relieve you at your post, and that will leave you free to deliver the message. Okay?"

"But I'm supposed to be guarding you," the guard pointed out.

"Perfect. I can handle that."

"Well . . ."

"There's a buck in it for you," Max said.

The guard brightened. "I could buy a whole box of gold stars," he said. "I'll do it."

Max gave the guard the message and a dollar, and the guard handed Max his rifle. Then Max assumed the watch over himself, and the guard departed to deliver the message.

As the guard was approaching the ballet dancer place, he met another guard. In fact, they collided at a corner.

"Watch it, you clumsy Arab," Max's guard grumbled. "I'm carrying an important message to the new ballet dancer from the American Advisor."

"Big deal, you camel's hump," the other guard replied. "It just so happens that I am carrying a double-important message to the American Advisor from the new ballet dancer."

"My message is triple-important," Max's guard retorted. "I didn't mention it only because I'm not the type to brag."

"May the Golden Peacock of Paradise drop bread crumbs in your ear," the other guard snarled.

"May the Emperor's horse swish his tail in your face!" Max's guard responded.

"May the full moon fall from Heaven and land in your soup bowl!" the other guard growled.

"May the seventh son of your seventh son flunk math!" Max's guard said nastily.

"Hey! That's an awful thing to say!" the other guard winced.

"Sorry about that," Max's guard replied apologetically. "I guess I kind of lost my head. Are we still friends?"

"You know the rule," the other guard said. "When two good friends insult each other, in order to become good friends again they have to exchange gifts. What do you have to give?"

"What do *you* have to give?" Max's guard replied warily.

"I got a buck for delivering this message," the other guard said.

"Me, too."

"We could exchange dollars."

Max's guard shook his head. "I need this buck. I'm going to buy myself a box of gold stars."

"Well . . . let's see . . . what else do we have?"

"We have the messages," Max's guard pointed out.

"Just the thing!" the other guard beamed.

The two guards exchanged messages, then parted, each guard going his own way, the best of friends once more.

Thus, it was written that Max received the message he had sent to 99, and 99 received the message that she had sent to Max. Max's message, which he received himself, read: Will meet you at the ballet dancer place. And 99's message, which she received herself, read: I will meet you at the wall.

Late that evening, Max slipped out of his room, nodded amiably to the guard, then made his way stealthily toward the ballet dancer place.

At the same time, 99 slipped out of the ballet dancer place, nodded amiably to the guard, then made her way stealthily toward the wall.

Reaching the ballet dancer place, Max nodded amiably to the guard, then rapped lightly on the door.

The knock was answered by another of the female ballet dancers.

"I'm looking for 99," Max whispered.

"You're in the wrong place," the girl whispered back. "There are only sixteen of us here."

"You don't understand," Max whispered. "I'm looking for the new flung."

"Oh. She just stepped out. Would you like to come in and wait?"

Max entered, and the girl closed the door.

"We're having a practice session," the girl said. "You can watch if you want to. But you can't stay very long. Dr. Yeh! is due soon. He stops in every evening to watch us practice. And I don't think he'd like it if he found a man in the ballet dancer place."

"Uh, the new flung, did she say when she'd be back?" Max asked.

The girl giggled.

"Pardon?" Max said.

"What a character—the new flung," the girl replied. "She told us a wild story about being a secret agent and having a rendezvous with another secret agent. She's probably meeting a boy friend. Who knows when she'll be back?"

"Oh. Well, in that case—"

"Hssst!" another ballet dancer interrupted. "Dr. Yeh! is coming!"

The first ballet dancer pushed Max toward the door. "Out! He mustn't find you here!"

"No! Not that way!" the second ballet dancer cried. "He'll run right into Dr. Yeh!"

"He can't leave!" a third ballet dancer said. "Disguise him!"

"How?" the second dancer asked.

"Give him a mop and let him pretend to be the cleaning woman," a fourth ballet dancer suggested.

"We don't have a cleaning woman. You know how atrocious the servant problem is," the second ballet dancer said.

"I do a pretty good imitation of Jimmy Cagney doing a fair imitation of Edward G. Robinson," Max said. "Do you think that would fool him?"

"The mop!" a twelfth ballet dancer said.

Max shook his head. "I do a lousy imitation of a mop."

"Put the mop on his head and dress him in tights and he'll look like one of us," the twelfth ballet dancer explained.

At that moment, there was a knock at the door.

"It's him! It's Dr. Yeh!" the ballet dancers cried in unison.

The second ballet dancer snatched up a pair of tights and the mop. She shoved them into Max's hands, then shoved Max into a closet. "Dress!" she hissed. "You're our new flung!"

"But I—"

The door slammed.

Inside the closet, Max grudgingly changed into the tights and mop. Through the door, he could hear Dr. Yeh! in conversation with the ballet dancers.

"Where is the new flung?" he heard Dr. Yeh! ask.

"She'll be right out," a ballet dancer replied.

"This is a great night for me," Dr. Yeh! said. "How long has it been since my troupe last had a flung to fling? It seems like weeks."

"It's been weeks," a ballet dancer confirmed.

Max opened the closet door and stepped out.

"Ah!" Dr. Yeh! cried happily. "Here is our new—" He stared. "This is our new flung?" he continued. He approached Max. "You look different," he said. "I don't recall that you had a handle in your hair."

"Oh . . . that," Max said, glancing back over his shoulder at the mop handle. "Actually, you see, that isn't a handle. It's a new technical advance in flung-wear. It's what you might call a rudder. We flungs were being flung into the air and losing our course. The rudder keeps us on the straight and narrow."

"Didn't you have dark hair before?" Dr. Yeh! said, squinting at Max puzzledly.

"It suddenly turned mop water gray," Max explained. "It happens quite often to us flungs. We're tossed high in the air, and, unfortunately, sometimes we look down. It's scarey. Enough to turn anybody's hair mop water gray."

Dr. Yeh! shrugged. "On with the ballet!"

The ballet dancers, taking Max with them, moved to the center of the room. Dr. Yeh! seated himself on the collapsible throne he had brought along.

"Just relax," one of the ballet dancers whispered to Max. "We'll do all the work. You just fly."

"Fine," Max whispered back. "I think I can handle— Fly?"

"There's nothing to it. Just—"

"On with the ballet!" Dr. Yeh! shouted.

One of the dancers stepped forward, facing Dr. Yeh! "This is a new routine we've worked out," she announced. "It's titled 'The Birth, Life and Death of the Count of Monte Cristo as performed by Mr. Feldstein's Social Studies students at Fairfield Elementary School and directed by Lewis and Clark while Lewis plays "A Hard Day's Night" on the lefthanded piccolo and Clark whistles the Second Movement from Daniel Webster's fugue for adverbs, verbs, pronouns, adjectives and kettle drums blues.' "

Dr. Yeh! applauded. "Snappy title," he said. "What's it about?"

"We haven't worked that out yet," the dancer replied. "We're still sort of ad-libbing."

"Good. I like surprises," Dr. Yeh! said. "On with the ballet!"

The troupe split into two groups. One group, including Max, remained at the left side of the room. The other group moved to the right side of the room.

"Allez-oop!" cried a dancer on the right side of the room.

At the signal, the dancers on the left side of the room lifted Max from the floor and threw him high into the air.

He landed with a plop in the middle of the room, right between the two groups of dancers.

"It's good," Dr. Yeh! said. "But it doesn't live up to the title yet. Needs work."

Painfully, Max got to his feet. As he did, he was swooped up by one of the groups of dancers. Again, they lifted him into the air. Holding him aloft, they bounded about the room.

"I see it! I see it!" Dr. Yeh! cried excitedly. "That's Lewis playing the piccolo!"

The dancers put Max on his feet and twirled him around. His mop handle swung wide and dropped three of the dancers, leaving them prostrate.

"Ho! The Count of Monte Cristo!" Dr. Yeh! exulted. "I'd recognize him anywhere!"

Once more the dancers scooped Max up and raised him high. Then, swinging him low, two grabbed his arms, two grabbed his legs, and one grabbed his mop handle, and, again, they flung him toward the opposite side of the room.

Max landed in the middle—minus the mop.

"Impostor!" Dr. Yeh! cried, leaping to his feet.

"Just in time," Max groaned, rising. "One more fling and I'd've been an ex-flung."

"What are you doing in my ballet dancer place!" Dr. Yeh! raged, confronting Max.

Max faced him squarely. "Would you believe that I was waiting for the 7:07 to Hackensack?"

"Absolutely not! There *is* no 7:07 to Hackensack. The 7:07 goes to Darien."

"Then would you believe that I was looking for the airport and took a wrong turn at the oasis?"

"It wouldn't make any difference whether I believed you or not," Dr. Yeh! replied. "The penalty for getting caught in the ballet dancer place is death. That's the rule, whether you've got a good reason or not. To the wall!" he shouted.

"Just a minute," Max said. "You mean you're going to take me out to the wall, stand me up in front of a firing squad and execute me?"

"Is that what that means?" Dr. Yeh! replied.

"As I understand it, yes," Max nodded.

"Then that's what I'm going to do," Dr. Yeh! said. He went to the door, opened it, and called out. "Guards! To the wall!"

There was a clatter of bootsteps outside. But no guards appeared.

"No! No! No! Not you!" Dr. Yeh! screamed down the corridor. "Him! He goes to the wall, not you! Come back here!"

Again there was the clatter of bootsteps. Then a half-dozen guards burst into the room and seized Max.

"Just one second!" Max said crisply. "As I recall, according to the rules of execution, the doomed man is entitled to a last request."

"Later," Dr. Yeh! said. "After the execution."

"Later will be too late," Max objected. "I demand

that I be allowed to change back into my other clothes."
He popped the elastic of his tights. "I wouldn't be
caught dead in an outfit like this," he said.

"Request granted," Dr. Yeh! said grudgingly. "But
hurry it up."

Max stepped into the closet. Inside, with the door
closed, he opened the satchel and looked for a gadget
that might help him escape. Soon he found a gadget
that was labeled "For Use When Trapped in a Closet."
It looked like a skeleton key.

"Obviously, it's not really a skeleton key," Max said
softly to himself. "When inserted in the keyhole it
probably expels a smoke screen that confuses the adversary and allows the user to escape under the cover
of fog."

Max inserted the key into the lock, then turned it.
The door creaked slowly open. That was all.

"Well, are you coming?" Dr. Yeh! demanded.

"Don't nag!" Max snapped.

He closed the door, dropped the skeleton key back
into the bag, changed clothes, then stepped out.

Once more the guards seized him. They dragged him
toward the doorway. Dr. Yeh! tagged along.

"I have one other last request," Max said, as the
guards hustled him along the corridor. "There's a little
chili joint called 'Mexican Fred's' in lower Manhattan.
I'd like to have one more bowl of Mexican Fred's chili
before I die."

Dr. Yeh! shuddered. "I know the place," he said.
"By refusing your request, I'm doing you a favor. That
stuff could kill you."

They reached the courtyard, and the guards dragged
Max to the wall.

99 was there, still waiting. "Max! Where have you
been?" she demanded irritably.

"Where I've been isn't terribly important to me right
now," Max replied. "The important question is: Where

am I going? At a time like this, a fellow begins to wonder."

"Max—are you in some sort of trouble?" 99 asked worriedly.

He pointed to the guards, who, a short distance away, were trying to form a straight line. "You are about to witness an execution, 99," he replied. "Mine." He handed her the satchel. "You better hold this. I might drop it when I fall."

"Oh, Max, no!" 99 cried. "Isn't there something I can do?"

"Well . . . there's a little joint in lower Manhattan called 'Mexican Fred's.' What you could do, 99, is—"

"Ready!" Dr. Yeh! commanded the guards.

They raised their rifles.

"It's probably too late," Max said to 99. "Besides, the chili would undoubtedly be cold by the time you got it back here."

"Aim!" Dr. Yeh! commanded.

Max addressed one of the guards. "A little bit to the left," he said, gesturing. "As it is, you're going to miss me by a mile."

The guard adjusted his aim.

"No . . . too far," Max said. "Just a squinch back to the right."

Again the guard adjusted his aim.

"Right on target!" Max said approvingly.

Dr. Yeh! stormed up to Max. "Who's directing this execution?" he demanded. "You or me?"

"Sorry about that," Max replied.

"You think you're so hot!" Dr. Yeh! barked. "You want me to come over here and stand by the wall and you go over there and give the orders? Is that what you want?"

"No, no, I apologize," Max said. "You're doing fine, fine. I'm sorry I interrupted."

"Just butt out, that's all!"

"I told you—I'm sorry."

Dr. Yeh! stomped back to his place at the end of the line of guards.

"Sorehead," Max muttered.

"Aim!" Dr. Yeh! bellowed.

"You said that," Max pointed out.

Dr. Yeh! shook an outraged finger at him. "I'm warning you! One more word, and you're gonna get it!"

Max turned to 99. "He's right, you know. The word is 'fire.' "

"Max! What can I do!"

"Try the black bag," Max suggested. "Look for something labeled 'For Use at Executions.' "

Hurriedly, 99 rummaged through the bag. "Here!" she cried excitedly, extracting a gadget.

"99, that's a cigarette lighter."

"I know. But it says, 'For Use at Executions.' Just a second, I'll read the instructions. It says, 'When you are standing at the wall and you are offered a last cigarette, use this gadget to light it.' "

"Somehow, I expected a little more from R & D," Max said disappointedly.

"Max, maybe the instructions are a ruse. Maybe the cigarette lighter is something more than a cigarette lighter."

"Yes, it might expel a smoke screen," Max replied. "I don't suppose, at this point, it will do any harm to try it."

Quickly, 99 aimed the cigarette lighter at the guards and pressed the button.

"Fire!" Dr. Yeh! shouted.

The guards instantly dropped their rifles, wailed, "Magic! Magic!" and fell to their knees.

Baffled, Max stared at the prostrate guards.

99 stared at the flame that the lighter had produced.

Dr. Yeh! rushed up to Max. "Magic!" he gushed happily.

Max felt his body. "Did they all miss?" he asked.

"They didn't shoot," Dr. Yeh! replied. "They were too astounded. It's Magic!"

"But I heard you yell 'fire!' " Max said.

"I didn't yell 'fire!' " Dr. Yeh! replied. "I yelled 'fire!' "

"Oh . . . is there a difference?"

"When I yelled 'fire!' I wasn't ordering them to fire, I was exclaiming over the fire," Dr. Yeh! said, indicating the lighter flame.

Max smiled. "Oh, yes, now I understand. I forgot there for a second that I'm among ignorant savages. When you saw the flame appear, you thought it was magic. The fact is, however, that that gadget is a quite common ordinary little gadget in civilized societies. There's no magic to it."

"Look who's calling who an ignorant savage," Dr. Yeh! replied. "What you don't know about cigarette lighters! This one works the first time the button is pushed. That's Magic!"

"Unusual, yes," Max agreed. "But magic? I frankly—"

"Who's the sheik around here!" Dr. Yeh! snarled. "I say it's Magic!"

"All right. We won't debate the matter," Max said. "I think we've held up the execution long enough. Now, if you'll just get those guards to their feet, and if you'll just return to your own—"

"You're trying to run the show again!" Dr. Yeh! said warningly.

Max raised his hands in a gesture of apology.

"The execution is off!" Dr. Yeh! beamed. "Instead, we'll have a big party!"

"What's the occasion?" Max asked.

"Who needs an excuse for a party?" Dr. Yeh! replied. He turned to 99. "Flung," he ordered, "return to the ballet dancer place. Get the flingers together and report to my throne room. Tell them it's Party Time. My

American Advisor and I wish to be entertained. We will feast and we will tell tall stories and we will watch the ballet. And then—" He winked at Max. "—we will open the black bag and play marbles with the money!"

"Max . . . ?" 99 said.

"Do what you're told, flung," Max replied.

99 scurried off. She was still carrying the black bag.

"Shall we adjourn to the throne room, American Advisor?" Dr. Yeh! smiled, putting an arm around Max's shoulder.

"Why not?" Max replied. "It beats the firing squad."

4.

By the time Max and Dr. Yeh! reached the throne room it had already been transformed into a banquet hall. A sumptuous, banquet-style meal awaited them—chicken à la king, stale rolls, peas, stuffed celery, canned peaches, and warm milk. And not long after they had seated themselves at the table, the ballet troupe appeared.

"On with the ballet!" Dr. Yeh! cried.

The ballet began. 99 was the center of attraction. The flingers flung her from one side of the banquet hall to the other, always catching her just before she hit the floor.

"It's magnificent," Max said, not really paying much attention, but looking around for some place to plant a pellet.

"It's good, yes," Dr. Yeh! frowned. "But there's something not quite right about that new flung."

Max peered at 99, who was, at that moment, sailing through the air. "Maybe it's because she's carrying that black satchel," he said.

"I think that's it," Dr. Yeh! agreed. "Somehow, it detracts from the usual grace of the dance."

"It'll do it every time," Max said. "You get a ballet dancer carrying a suitcase and she's all thumbs."

Dr. Yeh! suddenly tugged at Max's sleeve. "Watch! This is the climax!" he said.

Max concentrated on the gyrations of the dancers. He saw the flingers hurl the flung high into the air. Oddly, she appeared to be headed straight for the table.

"I think we're going to have a guest," Max said. "You should have set another place."

"No. You see——"

At that moment, the flung hit the table. And Max understood why it would have been pointless to set another place. As the flung skidded toward them along the table top she cleared everything from her path, dishes, food and all. Then, as if it had been planned that way, she came to a stop directly in front of Max and Dr. Yeh!

"Magnifico!" Dr. Yeh! applauded.

Max removed his plate of chicken à la king from his lap. "Frankly, I've seen neater landings," he said.

"Sorry about that, Max," 99 apologized.

"Flung, you performed stupendously!" Dr. Yeh! said to 99. "And, as is the custom, to celebrate your triumph, you and I will exchange gifts."

"Gee, I don't really have much to give," 99 said.

"You need only a bauble," Dr. Yeh! replied. "According to the custom, when the sheik (that's me) is pleased, he gives his most valuable possession to the one who has pleased him. And, in return, that person presents the sheik (that's me) with a trinket of no worth at all." He indicated Max. "This is my gift to you," he said. "I make you a present of my American Advisor."

"So much!" 99 gasped.

"It's not *that* much," Dr. Yeh! replied. "Soon we will

open the black bag, and, after that, he will be of no use to me, anyway. Advice, I can get anywhere." He smiled expectantly. "And now, what do you have for me?"

"Well . . ." 99 took a string of beads from around her neck. ". . . I do have these."

"Perfect!" Dr. Yeh! beamed. "What could be more worthless to a sheik (that's me)?"

99 placed the string of beads around Dr. Yeh!'s neck. "May I take my gift with me?" she asked.

"You don't want it wrapped?"

99 shook her head. "I'll carry it. I have a helicopter waiting right outside."

Dr. Yeh! giggled. "Not only is she a talented flung, she's got a sense of humor," he said.

99 got Max by the hand. "Let's go, Max!"

He resisted. "Not now, 99! Duty first."

"Go with her," Dr. Yeh! commanded. "But leave the black bag."

"Oh, well, I have to take the bag with me," 99 said. "I have my change of clothes in it. But I'll bring it back later."

Dr. Yeh! smiled again, but sinisterly this time. "Take the clothes out, and leave the bag here," he said.

99 clung to the bag. "Max!" she hissed, tugging at him.

"No, 99!" he replied adamantly. "Plant first, run second."

"Max," she said grimly, "the pea has been planted!"

"Oh?" he replied, puzzled.

"What is that—the pea has been planted?" Dr. Yeh! scowled. "Some kind of code?"

"Yes, code," Max replied. "You misunderstood what she said because of the code—the code in her head." He turned to 99. "Sneeze," he ordered.

99 sneezed.

"Something very strange is going on here," Dr. Yeh! said. "But, I'll overlook it. Just hand me the black bag."

"Max!"

"Right, 99—run!"

Max and 99 dashed toward the exit, with 99 still hanging onto the black satchel.

"Guards!" Dr. Yeh! shouted.

Guards suddenly rushed in through the doorway.

"Seize them!" Dr. Yeh! cried.

Max and 99 whipped around and raced in the opposite direction. They charged through the doorway that led to the ballet dancer place.

"After them! Get the black bag!" they heard Dr. Yeh! shout.

"That way!" Max said, pointing toward a stairway.

They dashed up the stairs. Behind them they could hear the clatter of bootsteps. Another flight of stairs appeared, and they hurried upward once more. The clatter of bootsteps came nearer. They scrambled up another flight of stairs, then another. Then they reached a dead end.

"Max! What now?" 99 wailed.

Max ran to a sculpture of a ballet dancer. He pushed down on the dancer's outstretched leg. The wall that formed a deadend suddenly rose, revealing an entrance to the roof. Quickly, Max picked up the sculpture, and he and 99 dashed through the opening. When they reached the roof, Max put the sculpture down, then quickly raised its leg. The wall lowered, sealing the opening.

"Wonderful! They can't get to us!" 99 said.

"Not as long as we have this sculpture," Max smiled. "I think we defeated them, 99. They're in there, on the other side of the wall, and we're out here—" His enthusiasm suddenly diminished. "—trapped on the roof," he concluded glumly.

The guards began hammering on the wall.

"Max, that wall won't hold out forever," 99 said. "What do we do now?"

Max went to the edge of the roof and looked down. He shook his head, backing away. "No, we can't do that."

"If only we could contact the helicopter," 99 said.

"Yes, if only we could—99! That's it!" Hurriedly, he took off his shoe, then dialed.

Operator: Sorry, you have dialed a wrong number.

Max: Operator, I didn't dial a wrong number. I dialled Operator, and I got you.

Operator: The way I look at it, that's a wrong number. Every time somebody dials Operator, I have to answer. And it's always right when I'm doing my nails.

Max: Sorry about that, Operator. But this is an emergency.

Operator: Oh, is that you, Maxie? How's our shoe?

Max: Your shoe is fine, Operator. Now look, I want to contact a helicopter. I know the helicopter doesn't have a telephone, but it does have a radio. So, if you could connect my telephone to the helicopter's radio, then I and the pilot could converse.

Operator: You're a real nut, aren't you, Maxie?

Max: Operator, would you mind? This is an emergency. The guards are hammering on the door.

Operator: Okay, Maxie, I'll try it. I can't do anything else 'til my nails dry, anyway. Where is this helicopter?

Max (pointing): Right over there behind that sand dune.

Operator: Could you get a little more clear, Maxie. Like name the desert, maybe?

Max: Sahara. And please hurry, Operator.

Operator: That's all the way across the ocean. It'll take time. Radio signals don't move so fast when they have to swim, you know.

Max: Operator, please!
                    (crackling sounds)

Lance Chalfont: Lance Chalfont, silent birdman, here.

Max: Lance, this is Max Smart!

Lance Chalfont: No kiddin'. How'd you get inside that itty-bitty radio, Max?

Max: Now, listen carefully, Lance. I am not inside the radio. I am on the roof of the KAOS Science Laboratory. 99 and I are trapped out here. We want you to rescue us.

Lance Chalfont: Well, I'll try, Max. How do I get there? Is there some kind of a ladder?

Max: No, but there's a stair. You take the corridor to—No, Lance, what I mean is, I want you to use the helicopter to rescue us.

Lance Chalfont: Max, you know how big this helicopter is. I couldn't get it up no stairs.

Max: Think, Lance. What does a helicopter do? It flies, right? I want you to fly the helicopter to the roof, pick us up, then fly away. Got that?

Lance Chalfont: Nobody don't have to draw no pictures for Lance Chalfont. I'll be there in a jiffy, Max.
                    (crackling sounds)

Operator: How did I do, Maxie?

Max: Excellent, Operator. If we escape, it will be your doing.

Operator: Then do a little favor for me, Maxie, will you? Don't get sand in our shoe.

Max: I promise, Operator.

Max hung up.

"Max, the guards are breaking down the wall," 99 said. "Where is the helicopter?"

"Well, according to my calculations, the heli—"

There was a roaring sound overhead.

"—copter ought to be arriving right now."

"Max! The wall!"

As the wall gave way and a flood of guards poured onto the roof, the helicopter settled down beside Max and 99.

Max and 99 scrambled aboard. There was the sound of a volley of shots. Bullets pinged by their ears.

"Upward and onward!" Max cried.

The helicopter zoomed heavenward. A moment later it was safely out of range of the guards' rifles.

"That was close!" Max breathed.

"Got the job done, though, eh?" Lance Chalfont said. "Planted that itty-bitty pea just like you was told to, right?"

"That we did," Max smiled.

"Howja do it?" Lance Chalfont asked.

"Actually, it was very simple," Max replied. "We—" He turned to 99. "How *did* we do it, 99?"

"Well, Max, you remember that necklace I presented to Dr. Yeh!?" 99 replied. "Did you notice anything familiar about it?"

"Familiar? No. Frankly, it wasn't to my taste, though. It looked like a bunch of strung-together peas."

"That's it, Max. It was. I strung some pellets together, making a necklace of them."

"Then—"

"Yes. Dr. Yeh! is wearing the explosives around his neck," 99 said. "I imagine that as soon as he gets to his quarters, he'll put the necklace in his jewel box, and . . . our pellets will be planted."

Max turned back to Lance Chalfont. "See? I told you it was simple."

"Max," 99 said, "shouldn't we check in with the Chief?"

"Right," Max replied, removing his shoe and dialing.

Operator: One moment, please. I am ringing your helicopter.

Max: No, no, Operator. That emergency is over. I want to talk to the Chief, now.

Operator: One moment, please. I am ringing your Chief.

Chief: Control. Chief speaking.

Max: Chief, it's me. I am happy to report that the first explosive has been planted. Anything new at Headquarters?

Chief: Only this, Max. The KAOS agent has also planted his first pellet. He was observed slipping away from our Science Lab. We're making a search for the explosive, but we don't have much hope of finding it.

Max: In other words, Chief, at this juncture, the race is a tie.

Chief: Yes, that's the way it stands, Max. Haste is all important now. The fate of Control depends on it— and on you and 99, Max.

Max: We're already speeding to the next KAOS installation, Chief. I'll call you when I have something further to report.

Max hung up, then settled back in his seat. "I told the Chief that we're speeding to our next destination," he said to 99.

She nodded. "I heard you."

"I heard that, too," Lance Chalfont said. "Kinda confused me."

"Oh? How so?" Max asked.

"Me and the helicopter, we're just flyin' around in circles," Lance Chalfont replied. "Ain't nobody told us where to go."

"Tell him where to go, Max," 99 said.

"For the sake of pleasant relations, I think, instead, I'll just give him our next destination," Max replied, opening the satchel and getting out a fact sheet. He studied the paper a moment, then said, "Head straight for the middle of the Atlantic Ocean, Lance. Our next destination is KAOS's undersea weapons arsenal."

"Which way's that?" Lance Chalfont asked.

Max pointed. "Thataway."

As the helicopter sped over the water, Max and 99 studied the fact sheet on the KAOS weapons arsenal. "This will be a tough one," Max said. "The arsenal is commanded by the infamous Dr. Gill."

"Haven't I heard that name before?" 99 frowned.

"Yes, it's infamous," Max replied. "Dr. Gill, you know, is half man and half fish."

"Which half is which?" 99 asked.

Max thought for a second. "The upper half must be a fish," he replied. "It doesn't say anything in the fact sheet about him having a tail. What he has done, you see, over a period of years, is conditioned himself to living under water. His lungs act as a storage tank for fresh air, allowing him to breathe without the assistance of an auxiliary air supply."

"What's that mean?" Lance Chalfont asked.

"He can breathe under water," Max replied.

"Shucks, I can do that, too," Lance Chalfont said. "Only trouble is, when I try it, I durn near drown."

"That's the difference," Max pointed out. "Dr. Gill doesn't drown."

"Sakes alive!" Lance Chalfont said. "He must be half fish and half man."

"But we're not," 99 said to Max. "How will we get inside the installation?"

"Headquarters has undoubtedly considered that," Max replied. He opened the black satchel and began rummaging through it. "We will probably find equipment in here that will— Ah, yes!" He brought out two small packages. "Here we are. These packages are labeled 'Diving Gear.' "

Max and 99 opened the packages.

"Here's a wet suit," Max said, "and here's a— A clothespin?"

"You put that on your nose, so you can keep your hands free," 99 said. "It explains that in the instructions."

"Well, it's probably not the latest thing, but it'll have to do," Max said.

"Thar she blows!" Lance Chalfont shouted.

"What?"

"The middle of the ocean," Lance Chalfont replied, pointing.

Max and 99 looked out the window.

"Where?" 99 asked.

"Right there," Max answered. "Right where that X is. See it?"

"Oh . . . yes."

Max and 99 slipped into their wet suits and pinned the clothespins to their noses. Then the helicopter descended until it was hovering over the X.

"I'll be waitin' right here," Lance Chalfont said, "keepin' my meter runnin'. That's a little silent birdman joke."

"We know," Max nodded. He turned to 99. "Ready?"

"Ready, Max."

"Close your eyes," Max said. Then, to Lance Chalfont, he called out, "Now!"

Lance Chalfont tipped the helicopter and Max and 99 tumbled out the open doorway.

A second later, they hit the water, then bobbed to the surface. After taking in a deep breath, they dived. And seconds after that they reached the installation's exhaust outlet and crawled through it, reaching the inside, where fresh air was available again.

Max and 99 exhaled, then inhaled, taking in deep breaths.

"Safe!" 99 sighed.

"Doomed!" an unfamiliar voice boomed.

Max and 99 peered through the dimness of the compartment. In the doorway they saw a large figure. Then the figure moved, approaching them. It was a small man, who had cast a large shadow. He, too, was wearing a wet suit. He was smiling sinisterly. Otherwise, he looked completely normal, except that his ears appeared not to be ears, but gills.

"Dr. Gill, I presume," Max said.

"Very good, for a wild guess," Dr. Gill replied.

"Let me introduce myself," Max said. "I am—"

"I know. You are Max Smart. And your companion is Agent 99. I recognized you the instant I saw you. I study the 'Wanted' posters sent out by KAOS. After all, there's not much else to do down here."

"Fine," Max said. "Now that that's settled, we can get down to business. And the first item on the agenda is a comment you made when we first entered your arsenal. 'Doomed' you said, I believe. Was there any particular significance to that statement?"

Dr. Gill smiled sinisterly again. "You are my prisoners," he replied. "And, in time, after I have toyed with you, I intend—naturally—to destroy you."

"All right, that explains the comment," Max said. "Now then, item number two. How do you intend to keep us prisoner? Do you have a band of armed cutthroats to guard us?"

"You will see," Dr. Gill replied, "that the whole installation, in a sense, is a cell. There is no need for guards. In fact, I am quite alone down here. At least, I was until you arrived."

"I see," Max nodded. "Then what is to stop me from hurling myself across the room at you, delivering a karate chop to a sensitive area of your person, rendering you unconscious, binding you, gagging you, then taking you back to Control with me as a prisoner?"

"Your distaste for violence?" Dr. Gill guessed.

Max shook his head. "As much as I dislike violence, I never hesitate to use it when it appears to be the simplest means of making a point."

"Then perhaps this will stop you," Dr. Gill smiled, showing Max and 99 a tiny pillbox-size gadget that he held in his hand.

"That's hard to believe," Max replied.

"Then I will demonstrate," Dr. Gill said. Holding up the gadget, he pressed a button on its side.

Nothing appeared to happen.

"Maybe the batteries are low," Max smiled.

But suddenly 99 clutched her throat. "Max! Air!"

Max responded immediately. He clutched his own throat. "99! Air!"

"Now, you understand," Dr. Gill said. "I shut off the air supply, which is controlled by this gadget. I am unaffected, however, as you can see. I have a store of air in my lungs that will last me almost indefinitely."

"I believe!" Max choked.

Dr. Gill pressed the button again. And a moment later Max and 99 were able to breathe once more.

"Is it clear now that you are my prisoners?" Dr. Gill said. "If you make any attempt at violence, or to escape, I will simply press the button, and you will suffocate in seconds."

"Yes, well, that seems pretty clear," Max replied. "But it does bring up a question. Why didn't you destroy us just then?"

Dr. Gill sighed sadly. "The truth is, Max, I am a lonely fish . . . uh, that is, man. I long for companionship. None of the KAOS agents will stay down here with me. I'm not good company, they say."

"Oh . . . why is that?" Max asked.

Dr. Gill grinned evilly. "I keep shutting off the air supply," he explained. "It's a nervous habit."

"If they were really your friends they would overlook little things like that," Max said. "I know if you were a

Control agent and you invited me to stay down here with you for a while, I certainly wouldn't crab about a minor inconvenience. Incidentally, have you ever thought of switching your allegiance to Control—where you'd be among true friends?"

"It's too late," Dr. Gill replied. "I'm in too deep."

"I see what you mean," Max replied.

"Now," Dr. Gill said, gesturing toward the doorway, "shall we have lunch? And enjoy a little polite conversation?"

"Is there any other choice?" Max asked.

Dr. Gill pressed the button on the gadget.

"Max! Air!" 99 cried.

"99! Air!" Max choked.

Dr. Gill pressed the button again. "Never question my suggestions," he warned. "It irritates my nervous habit."

"We'll try to remember that," Max panted.

5.

DR. GILL led the way out of the compartment. Max and 99 followed him at a short distance.

"Look for a place to plant the explosive," Max whispered.

"There isn't any place, Max! These steel walls and this steel floor and this steel ceiling, and no furnishings. He lives like a hermit."

"Yes, the old crab."

A few moments later, Dr. Gill ushered them into his kitchen. It was adequately furnished, but, at first glance, there didn't appear to be a hiding place for the pellet.

"Please be seated," Dr. Gill said, gesturing toward the table and chairs. "I'll prepare lunch. Is there, by any chance, anything special you'd like?"

"How about lobster?" Max suggested.

Dr. Gill stiffened and looked at him coldly. "You're suggesting cannibalism, Mr. Smart!" he snapped. "The lobster is one of my own kind!"

"Sorry about that," Max replied meekly. "We'll eat anything you prepare."

"Good, good. I picked some fresh seaweed this morning," Dr. Gill said. "It grows wild down here, you know."

"I don't blame it," Max replied. "Trapped in the
ocean, I'd probably grow a little wild myself."

Dr. Gill reached for the gadget he had placed on the
counter.

"Ah-ah! Nothing personal!" Max said quickly.

"Careful," Dr. Gill warned. "I don't want to have to
destroy you at table. It would spoil my lunch."

"And what kind of a guest would that make me!"
Max said.

Dr. Gill brought plates to the table, then returned
to the counter. A moment later he came back with a pot.
He dipped seaweed from it, using a three-pronged fork,
and dropped large portions onto the plates.

"Ah . . . I think you overlooked something," Max
said. "It's raw."

Dr. Gill laughed. "Who ever heard of cooking seaweed? It would ruin it."

"Oh. Well then, if you'll just give me a fork, I'll dig
right in."

"Fork!" Dr. Gill glared. "You don't fork seaweed!
You approach it lying flat on your tummy, flap your
fins, and nibble at it! Where did you learn your table
manners?"

After lunch, Dr. Gill took Max and 99 on a tour of
the installation. First he showed them the ventilating
system.

"I pump in air from the surface through this pipe,"
he explained. "The air then passes through this bubble
bath."

Max and 99 stared at the glass tank, in which bubbles
were bobbing around, obviously circulated by a flow
of air.

"Bubble bath?" 99 said curiously.

"To purify the air," Dr. Gill explained. "You can't

imagine how dirty the air is on the surface. Ships use it, birds use it, helicopters use it. It's full of fumes. Gasoline fumes, atom fumes, feather fumes. Ugh!"

"What happens to the air after it's purified?" Max asked.

"Aren't you going to ask me what kind of bubbles those are?" Dr. Gill countered.

"No. I can see. They're soap bubbles."

Dr. Gill shook his head, smiling. "They're plastic bubbles," he said. "Scientifically, I'm far ahead of the outside world. Outside, they're still using old-fashioned soap to make bubbles. I've already switched to plastic."

"Very interesting," Max admitted. "*Now,* where does the air go after it has been purified by the plastic bubbles?"

"It comes out here," Dr. Gill replied, showing Max and 99 a pipe-like outlet. "It circulates through the installation, then is rejected through the exhaust system."

"Well, fine," Max nodded. "Now what?"

"My laboratory," Dr. Gill said, leading them on. "Believe it or not, I am growing a new variety of plants down here. I foresee the day when everybody will live under the seas. And I realize that not all of them will have a taste for seaweed. So . . ."

He opened a door and ushered them into a large room that looked much like a greenhouse. Plants, in shallow wooden boxes, were growing everywhere.

Dr. Gill escorted them down the rows. "These are my sea cabbages . . . these are my sea carrots . . . these are my sea spinaches . . . these are my sea peas . . . these are my sea—"

"Just a second," Max interrupted, reaching into the satchel. "I think one of your sea peas dropped on the floor."

Dr. Gill looked down. "I don't see it."

"Right here," Max said, reaching down, then rising, holding a pea-like pellet between his fingers.

Dr. Gill took the pea from him. "Case of weak stem," he frowned. "I'll have to look into that."

"Maybe you could glue it back onto the plant," Max suggested.

Dr. Gill shook his head. "No, it's useless now."

He tossed the pea into the air and it floated out of the room.

Max and 99 stared.

"How did it do that?" Max asked.

"It was caught by the flow of air," Dr. Gill explained. "As I told you, the air circulates, then is rejected by the exhaust system. Anything as light as a pea, if it isn't anchored to something heavier, is carried away by the air flow."

"Hmmmm."

The tour proceeded.

"These are my sea tomatoes," Dr. Gill said, pointing. "And these are my sea potatoes . . . and my sea rutabagas . . . and . . ."

Max dropped a pellet in among the rutabagas. It immediately floated away.

"Drat!"

"Pardon?" Dr. Gill said.

"I said, 'Drat's very interesting,'" Max replied. "You seem to have rations here to suit anybody's taste. Which is quite an accomplishment—for sea rations."

"Too bad you won't be around a few months from now," Dr. Gill said. "I'm cross-breeding some of these plants. I expect to produce sea lettabagas and sea carraches and sea tomapeas and sea spinatoes and all sorts of fascinating varieties."

"You intend to release us, then, eh?" Max said.

"You could call it that," Dr. Gill smiled. "I'll call it 'destroy'. But you can call it 'release' if you want to. You are fortunate that you were so impressed by my little garden. Otherwise, I would have destroyed you now. As it is, however, I will keep you around for a while. Later, you will join me at dinner. Then, after that, I will show you my garden again."

"I can hardly wait," Max said.

With Dr. Gill leading the way once more, they left the laboratory. A few moments later the three reached a cell.

"In here," Dr. Gill said, opening the door. "I'll keep you here until dinnertime."

Max and 99 entered the cell, and Dr. Gill closed and locked the door.

"There is no escape from this cell," Dr. Gill said. "But, even if you did get out, you couldn't escape from the installation. The exhaust outlet—the only way out —is located near my office. I would see you. And when I saw you, I would—"

He pressed the button on the gadget.

"Max! Air!" 99 gasped.

"99! Air!" Max choked.

Dr. Gill pressed the button again. "You get the idea," he grinned.

"You have nothing to worry about," Max told him. "We're just not the kind who eat and run."

Still grinning, Dr. Gill departed.

"Max! We're doomed!" 99 wailed.

"Not quite, 99!" Max replied. "This will come as a surprise to you, but, actually, I was lying when I said that we're not the type to eat and run."

"Max!"

"Considering the circumstance, I thought a little fib was pardonable," Max said.

"I agree, Max. But how are we going to get out of here?"

"Be a little more specific, 99. Out of the installation or out of the cell?"

"Both."

"Couldn't you limit it to 'out of the installation'? I know the answer to that."

"But, Max, if we can't get out of the cell, how can we get out of the installation?"

"There, 99, I think you have the nub of the problem," Max replied. "In fact, my guess is that we're doomed."

"Max! The black bag. Maybe there's something in the bag that will help us."

"Well, it's worth a look," Max said.

He opened the bag and began extracting gadgets. "Here's a collapsible shovel for digging out of a mud slide. And a collapsible compass for finding the side of the tree that the moss grows on. And a collapsible electric saw for sawing through the bars of a cell. And a collapsible—"

"Max!" 99 broke in. "That's it—the collapsible saw!"

Max shook his head. "Collapsible *electric* saw, 99," he pointed out. "As you can see, there's no electrical outlet in this cell."

"Oh . . . yes. Too bad. What else is there, Max?"

"Well, let's see. Collapsible electric power unit for operating collapsible electric saw for sawing through the bars of a cell if there is no electrical outlet in the cell. Say! that might come in handy!"

"Max! Quick! Saw through the bars!"

Max plugged in the saw. Then, "Oh-oh," he said.

"What is it, Max?"

"Unfortunately, this collapsible electric power unit has to be plugged into an electrical outlet."

"Oh . . ."

"Well, I guess R & D can't be expected to think of everything," Max said. "At least, they made a try." He began digging in the black bag again. "Here's a set of collapsible fins," he reported. "To be used when invited to a seaweed lunch. That's thoughtful—but a bit late. And here's—wait a minute, 99! Here's exactly what we need—a collapsible battery pack to operate a collapsible electric power unit for operating a collapsible electric saw for sawing through the bars of a cell when there is no electrical outlet in the cell. R & D *does* think of everything!"

"Marvelous, Max!"

Max plugged the electrical power unit into the battery pack, then plugged the electric saw into the electrical power unit. The motor whirred. But Max simply stared at the saw.

"Max . . . what is it?" 99 asked.

"99 . . . you know how the gadgets that R & D dreams up are not always what they appear to be?"

"Yes, Max . . ."

"It isn't a saw, 99. It's an electric toothbrush."

"Oh."

"Well, still, it'll come in handy," Max said. "As I recall, we didn't brush after lunch."

Max went back to the bag. He held up a tiny metal box. "Now, here's something for the man who has everything," he said. "A six-ounce container of super-activated rust."

"Rust, Max?"

"Yes, you know—the stuff that eats away iron bars."

"Max, if it eats away iron bars, why couldn't we—"

"Just a second, 99. I think I've just had an idea that may save our lives. If rust eats away iron bars, why can't we apply this rust to those iron bars? The rust will eat away the iron bars, and we'll be free!"

"Max, that's wonderful! Try it."

"I will. Just let me read the instructions. 'Apply rust to bars. Within a period of three to six years the rust will completely destroy the iron . . .' 99, I think I better keep looking."

"No, Max, read on," 99 said, looking over his shoulder.

"All right. 'In cases of emergency, the rusting process can be hurried by the use of heat. Note: friction creates heat.'"

"Max! We're saved!"

"We are?"

"Max, apply the rust to the bars, then brush the bars with the electric toothbrush. The brushing will cause friction, which will create heat."

Max thought a second, then replied, "99, I think I've got an idea. Why not apply this rust to the bars, then brush the bars with the electric toothbrush?"

"How will that help, Max?"

"Don't be a needler, 99," Max replied sourly. "Nobody likes a needler."

"Sorry about that, Max."

Max applied the rust to the bars, then switched on the electric toothbrush and began brushing the bars. Within minutes the bars had rusted away.

Max put all the items back into the black bag, then he and 99 stepped from the cell.

"What now, Max?" 99 asked.

"To the laboratory," Max replied. "We still have to plant the explosive."

They moved quietly along the corridor until they came to Dr. Gill's plant laboratory. Then, entering, they made their way along a row.

"Ah—here's what I want!" Max said.

"Max, that's a tomato plant."

Max opened the black bag. "As of now, it is," he said. "In about a second it will be a cross-breed—a peamato plant." He straightened, holding a tube. "In this tube," he explained, "I have cement. I'll simply glue this pellet—which looks like a pea—to the tomato plant, and when Dr. Gill sees it, he'll think he has a peamato."

"Good thinking, Max. And, of course, he'll take special care of it."

"Yes, until the whole thing blows up in his face," Max smiled.

Max glued the pellet to the tomato plant, then put

the cement back into the bag, and closed the bag. "Now, to escape from the installation," he said, leading the way out of the laboratory.

"How, Max?"

"Don't ask questions, 99. I have a theory. But if it were questioned too closely, I'm afraid I might find out that it won't work."

"I won't say a thing, Max."

Stealthily, they made their way along the corridor. Soon they reached the room that housed the ventilating system.

"Now, when I say 'now'," Max said, "you and I will hold onto the end of this pipe."

"This pipe where the air comes out?"

"Exactly."

"I don't see—"

"Please, 99, no questions."

"All right, Max."

Max reached up and turned a small wheel. "Now!" he said.

He and 99 grabbed hold of the pipe.

"Max—"

"That little wheel controls the air pressure," Max explained. "As you can see, air is now rushing into the tank—right?"

"Yes, I see, Max. But—"

"And what happens when you blow a lot of air into a bubble?" Max said.

"Well . . . it gets larger."

"You will note that the bubbles in the tank are growing larger. They are growing so large, in fact, that the tank cannot hold them. So, what will happen?"

"They'll burst."

Max shook his head. "Soap bubbles would burst," he said. "But these are plastic bubbles."

"Then they'll—"

"Right. The bubbles will be pushed out this pipe. When that happens—Ah—here comes one now. You'll see what will happen."

A film of plastic slowly emerged from the end of the pipe. As it did, it enveloped Max and 99, forming a gigantic bubble that enclosed them.

"Max!" 99 squeaked. "We're inside the bubble."

Max nodded smugly. "That's my theory," he said.

"But, Max—"

"Please! Don't question it!"

The bubble suddenly broke loose from the pipe. And, carried by the air flow, it floated toward the doorway.

"Now I understand!" 99 said. "We'll be carried out through the exhaust system in the bubble."

"Exactly."

"But, Max, there's one thing I don't under—"

"99, no! No, not yet!"

"All right, Max."

As the gigantic bubble floated toward the exhaust system, Dr. Gill suddenly rushed out of his office. He shouted at Max and 99, shaking his fist savagely. But, closed off by the plastic film, they couldn't hear him.

Raging, Dr. Gill punched the button on his gadget.

"Max! Air!" 99 gasped.

"There's no need for that, 99," Max replied calmly. "We have an air supply inside this bubble. Dr. Gill's control has no effect on it."

"Oh," 99 replied, free of panic.

"Wave goodbye to Dr. Gill," Max smiled.

99 waved.

Dr. Gill shook his fist again.

Then the bubble entered the exhaust system, emerged from the installation, and rose toward the surface.

"Max, that was brilliant," 99 gushed. "We're free."

"Not quite," Max pointed out. "We're still inside the bubble."

"Can't we puncture it?"

"I'm afraid not, 99. It's very thick, very durable plastic."

The bubble popped to the surface and floated. Overhead Max and 99 could see the helicopter hovering.

"Max, we're trapped!" 99 cried.

"I have one more theory, 99," Max replied. "Now—ask your question."

"My question?"

"Remember—when I told you my first theory, you had a question about it?"

"Oh . . . yes. Max, since we're heavier than the bubble, how will it float in the air? Won't our weight—"

The instant the question was out, the bubble burst, dropping Max and 99 into the water.

"Max! What happened!" 99 cried, floundering in the ocean.

"Well, my second theory was that my first theory wouldn't actually work," Max explained. "You see, that's what happens when a man has a theory, and his theory is questioned. It's proved to be wrong—and his bubble bursts."

99 shuddered. "Max . . . suppose your first theory had been right!" she said.

"Don't even think about it," Max replied. "In that case, we'd still be trapped down there in the installation. And, worse yet, we'd be having seaweed for dinner!"

The helicopter was hovering directly over them now.

"I'm throwin' down the ladder!" Lance Chalfont called.

"Throw away!" Max replied.

Lance Chalfont tossed a ladder out the open doorway. It hit the water and immediately sank.

"There's a joke on me!" Lance Chalfont hooted. "I shoulda held on to the other end!"

"Well, live and learn!" Max shouted back. "Try again with something else!"

"I'll throw a rope," Lance Chalfont replied.

"Throw away! But, first, tie the other end to something!"

"Gotcha, boy!"

Lance Chalfont disappeared from the opening for a moment, then reappeared, holding a coil of rope. He tossed it out the doorway.

Max caught the rope, and pulled, testing his weight against it. The rope gave. A picnic basket came through the opening, fell through the air, struck Max a glancing blow on the head, then disappeared below the surface.

"Let me guess what you tied the rope to," Max shouted.

"Did I do somethin' wrong, boy?"

"Get another rope," Max called. "Tie it to something that's anchored down. Tie it to a seat!"

"I'll tie it to your seat!" Lance Chalfont shouted back. "If I'm gonna lose a seat, I don't want it to be mine. That's how us silent birdmen fly, you know, by our seats."

"We're drowning!" Max bellowed. "Hurry!"

"Gotcha, boy!"

Lance Chalfont disappeared from sight once more. Then a second later he reappeared and tossed a second rope out the opening.

Max tested it and found it firm.

"Lady secret agents first," Max said, passing the rope to 99.

Minutes later, they reboarded the helicopter.

"Get your pea planted?" Lance Chalfont asked.

"Indeed we did," Max smiled. "Now, on to the next destination. Which is—" He opened the black satchel and got out a sheaf of papers. "—the KAOS training school in Switzerland," he announced. "Lance, do you think you can find Switzerland?"

"Sure. That's that place with them tall prairies."

"Mountains, you mean."

"Is that what they're called? No wonder they didn't

know what I was talkin' about that day I came draggin' back to the airport without my airplane! I told 'em I'd hit a tall prairie. They looked at me like I had my ailerons on backwards. I guess we just wasn't communicatin'."

"That was probably it," Max nodded.

"Well, here goes nothin'!" Lance Chalfont beamed, swinging the helicopter in the direction in which he guessed Switzerland might be.

"Max, shouldn't you report in?" 99 asked.

"Good idea, 99."

Max took off his shoe, poured ocean water from it, then dialed.

Operator: Max! Stop it!

Max (puzzledly): What did I do, Operator?

Operator: You got water all over me! It came pouring out of my receiver!

Max: Sorry about that, Operator. Will you connect me with the Chief now, please?

Operator: This is a $7.95 dress! It's ruined!

Max: I'll buy you a new dress, Operator.

Operator: With what? You can't even collect your overtime. They still owe you a $1.74, you know.

Max: All right, Operator. Put it on the bill—on Control's bill.

Chief: I heard that, Max. You're not authorized to put dresses on the phone bill.

Max: Then how about this, Chief? The Operator can charge her new dress to our phone bill, and when I get back to Headquarters, you can inform me that charging dresses to the phone bill is not allowed, and that you're going to take it out of my salary.

Chief: That may be the solution, Max. Operator, how does that sound to you?

Operator: I'll do it. So don't be surprised when you see a charge for a $20 dress on your phone bill.

Max: $20 dress, Operator? You said it was a $7.95 dress.

Operator: $12.05 for mental anguish. I'm sitting here in a wet dress.

Max: Oh.

Chief: Do you have anything to report, Max?

Max: Yes, Chief, I can report that 99 and I have successfully planted the second explosive. And, we are now on our way to the KAOS training school to plant the third explosive. How's that for action, Chief?

Chief: Not quite good enough, Max. The KAOS agent has already planted his second and third explosive and is on his way to the fourth installation.

Max (chagrined): Are you sure, Chief?

Chief: Well, a KAOS agent was seen slipping away from our undersea weapons arsenal and our training school.

Max: But are you positive that he's headed for our fourth installation? Maybe he'll stop for lunch.

Chief: That's possible, Max. Maybe you and 99 can skip lunch, and, in that way, catch up.

Max: Fine. That fits right in, Chief. It just so happens that Lance Chalfont threw the picnic basket into the ocean, anyway.

Chief: Good luck, Max!

Max: Thank you, Chief.

Operator: And, Max, take care of our shoe. Don't step on any tall prairies.

Max hung up.

6.

"THAR SHE blows!" Lance Chalfont cried.

Max and 99 looked out the front window. "Yes, that's it, that's the KAOS training school, all right," Max said.

Below, situated on a mountain peak, they saw a complex of ivy-covered stone buildings, surrounded by a high stone wall. They could see KAOS student agents moving about on the grounds.

"Sure surprises me," Lance Chalfont said. "You take a training school, a fella expects to see a lot of trains. Where you suppose they keep 'em? Downstairs?"

"I think you're attaching the wrong meaning to the term 'train,'" Max said. "In this case, train means to instruct. At this school, young men are trained—or instructed—in the methods used by KAOS. When they graduate, they are fully *train*ed KAOS agents. Now, do you understand?"

"Just about," Lance Chalfont replied. "There's just one thing I don't get. Where do they keep the trains?"

"Downstairs, I suspect," Max replied. He turned to 99. "Well, somehow we have to infiltrate that school," he said. "But, first, we have to get over the wall. And since we left our collapsible pole back there in the desert, we are faced with a bit of a sticky wicket. Do you have any suggestions?"

"Couldn't Lance Chalfont land us inside?" 99 said.

"Too noisy," Max replied. "We would be bound to attract attention."

"We could glide in," Lance Chalfont said. "To glide, what you do is, you just turn off the engine and glide."

"That's an idea," Max replied. "That would be quiet, anyway."

"They don't call me the silent birdman for nothin'," Lance Chalfont said.

Max pointed. "See that clear space behind that large building?" he said to Lance Chalfont. "Could you glide the helicopter down into that space?"

"Don't rightly know," Lance Chalfont replied. "I never glided this crate before. Every time I turned off the engine and tried to glide it just fell right smack-kaboom right out of the sky."

"Like a rock?" Max asked.

"Yup. Just like a wounded rock."

"In that case, we better think of something else," Max said.

"Max, why don't we parachute?" 99 said.

"Wait a minute! I just had an idea!" Max said. "We'll parachute!"

"Max—that's clever!" 99 applauded.

Max and 99 put on parachutes, then stood in the open doorway.

"Hover directly over that clear space behind that large building," Max said to Lance Chalfont. "We don't want to land among the students. They might suspect something."

"I'm hoverin'," Lance replied.

"Now!" Max cried.

Lance Chalfont tipped the helicopter and Max and

99 tumbled out and hurtled toward the ground. A moment later their chutes opened.

As they floated leisurely downward, side by side, Max opened the black satchel.

"Let's see what the old fact sheet has to say," he said, getting out a sheaf of papers.

"Max, I don't think we're going to land in that clear space," 99 said, looking down.

"Oh, we'll hit it all right," Max replied, looking at the fact sheet. "Let's see now . . . it says here that the KAOS training school is operated by The Professor. He—"

"Professor who, Max?"

"No, not Professor Who. Just plain 'The Professor'. He has no last name. According to the fact sheet, The Professor joined the faculty of the school when he was a young man. His name then was The Assistant Professor."

"Max . . ."

"Yes, 99?"

"Max, maybe his last name is 'Professor,' and his first name is 'The'. Maybe when he was younger he used his middle name, 'Assistant'. But then when he got the promotion he just dropped the middle name. That would explain—"

"99—if you don't mind—"

"Sorry, Max."

"To continue," Max went on. "Since entering the school as a young man, The Professor has not been off the grounds. As a result, he has no personal knowledge of the changes that have occurred in the outside world. When he is told of those changes, he quite often scoffs. The Professor, in other words, rejects the present, and idolizes the past."

"Max . . ."

"No more silly speculation on The Professor's last name, 99."

"No, Max. I just wanted to tell you that we're getting close to the ground."

Max looked down. "How do you like that!" he said disgustedly. "Somebody moved the school. We're coming down outside the wall!"

"I don't think anybody moved the school, Max. I think—"

"99, this is no time to argue details. Get ready to land!"

Max and 99 hit the ground simultaneously. 99 rolled gracefully and came up on her feet and began deflating her parachute, using the shroud lines. Meanwhile, Max rolled gracefully, but a bit too far, and came up standing on his head, after which he landed flat on his back. A second later, his parachute caught up with him and enveloped him. Max struggled to free himself of the yards of nylon cloth. The more he struggled, the more entangled he became.

"Max . . . are you all right?" 99 called.

"I'll be with you in a second, 99. I'm repacking my chute."

"From the inside, Max?"

"No one likes a needler, 99."

"Sorry, Max."

A moment later, Max crawled out from under the edge of the parachute. He got to his feet and dusted himself off. "Let that be a lesson to you, 99," he said. "That was a perfect demonstration of how not to land a parachute. I hope you were paying attention."

"I learned a lot, Max," 99 nodded.

"Now then, on to the school," Max said.

"Which way is it from here, Max? We landed so far away, I can't see it."

Max pointed upward. "It's right below that helicopter," he said. "Apparently the wind carried us off course. Shall we go, 99?"

They struck out through the underbrush, headed in the direction of the school.

"Max, why don't we use the road?" 99 asked.

"A secret agent always approaches the objective through the underbrush, 99. Don't you ever watch TV?"

"Max, couldn't we use the road until we get a little closer? *Then* we could cut through the underbrush."

Max halted and looked thoughtful. "I can't think of any rule that that would violate," he said finally. "We'll do it."

When they reached the road, they set out again in the direction of the school, using the hovering helicopter as a marker.

Max smiled. "Something very funny just occurred to me, 99," he said.

"What's that, Max?"

"I was just thinking that, although we haven't even reached the school yet, already we're drop-outs."

"Pardon, Max?"

"We jumped out of the helicopter in parachutes," Max explained. "We're drop-outs." He chuckled appreciatively.

"Wouldn't that make us jump-outs, Max?"

"99, you don't understand. It's a play on words. Parachutes. School. Drop-outs."

"But you said yourself that we jumped."

"Never mind, 99."

Soon the wall appeared. Once more, Max and 99 scrambled into the underbrush.

"There are guards everywhere," Max said. "I would say, roughly, that it's absolutely impossible to get inside the wall."

"But, Max, we have to. The fate of Control depends on it."

Max sighed. "Well, maybe something will come along."

"Max! Look! That's it. Those two young men coming along the road."

Max looked. "I knew something would come along," he said. "It always does on TV."

"They're headed for the school, Max. And they're walking along the road, in plain sight. That must mean that they're expected, that they won't have any trouble getting in."

Max's eyes narrowed. "If you'll look closely, 99," he said, "you'll see that those young men are walking along the road in plain sight. I'd go so far as to guess that they're expected, and won't have any trouble getting in."

"Max, I think you're right."

"What else do I think, 99?"

"Max, I think you think that if we waylay them we can take their places and get inside the wall without any trouble!"

"99, I think what you think I think is right."

As the two young men neared, Max and 99 pulled their pistols, then stepped out of the underbrush and confronted them.

"Greetings," Max said. "On your way to the KAOS training school, are you, young men?"

The two young men exchanged glances. Then the tall one replied, "Are you the welcoming committee?"

"You might say that," Max nodded. "Now, if you'll just step into the underbrush . . ."

"Is it some kind of a fraternity initiation?" the shorter of the two young men asked.

"You might say that, too," Max replied.

"You're probably going to bind us and gag us and leave us out here in the underbrush," the taller young man smiled. "That way, we'll be late reporting to the school and we'll be punished severely by the school authorities."

"Yes, you might say—"

"Great gag on us!" the smaller of the young men guffawed.

"It *is* pretty funny," Max smiled. "Now, will you step into the underbrush, please?"

Eagerly, the young men plunged into the underbrush.

"Bind and gag me first," the taller of the young men said. "I'm taller than he is."

"No, me first!" the shorter of the young men said. "He may be taller than I am, but I'm shorter than he is."

"Now, now, let's be fair about this," Max said. "We'll bind you and gag you both at the same time. I'll bind and gag you," he said to the tall one. "And, my cohort here will bind and gag you," he said to the short one.

"Couldn't it be the other way around?" the tall one said. "She looks like a faster binder and gagger than you."

"Now look," Max said irritably, "if we're going to have a lot of bickering about this, we'll just call the whole thing off."

The two young men immediately fell silent.

Max and 99 bound and gagged them, then took their identification papers.

"According to this I.D.," Max said, "I am now Ronald J. Macy, VII. Who are you, 99?"

"Arbuthnot L. Gimbel, Max."

"Hmmm . . . no wonder they didn't get along too well."

Max and 99 returned to the road, leaving the two young men in the underbrush, and approached the gate. A guard raised his musket and ordered them to halt.

"Musket?" Max said.

"The Professor keeps us armed with the latest weapons," the guard explained, examining Max's and 99's identification papers. "Next week we're getting Bowie knives."

"Are the papers all in order?" Max asked.

"They look fine," the guard replied. "Except on this

Gimbel, the sex is marked as 'male'. That couldn't be
right. Could it?" he said to 99.

"Heavens, no," 99 said.

"I didn't think so," the guard said. "You better have
that changed."

"It's too late," 99 replied. "I've been a female all
my life."

"He means have the identification paper changed,"
Max said.

"No, that wasn't what I meant," the guard said. "But
that's probably a better idea than what I had in mind."
He handed the identification papers back to Max and
99. "Pass Macy and Gimbel," he said.

Max and 99 entered the school grounds. Instantly,
they were set upon by a dozen or more young men who
were wearing red and white striped jackets. In the
lapels of the jackets were round metal buttons that
identified the young men as "Senior" students.

"You two are freshmen, aren't you?" the leader of
the seniors asked.

"That's right. This is our first day at the school,"
Max replied.

"Then you better start out right, obeying the rules,"
the leader said. "The first rule is: Whenever you see a
senior, snap to attention and turn your pockets inside-
out."

"That's an excellent rule," Max said. "I'm sure it's
based on careful consideration and sound judgment—
even if it does sound a little idiotic."

"Actually, it's very sensible," the leader said. "When
you turn your pockets inside-out, all the money falls
on the ground. We pick it up. That's the way we support
the Senior Fun."

"Senior *Fund,* you mean," Max corrected. "Like the
Community Fund . . . a charity."

"Not exactly," the leader said. "The Senior Fun is

used to finance the seniors when they go into town for a little fun." He held out a hand. "Cough up."

Max reached into his pocket, got out a dollar, and dropped it into the hand.

99 did the same.

"Carry on!" the leader commanded.

Max and 99 proceeded, heading toward what looked like the administration building.

"Now then," Max said, "all we have to do is find some place to plant the explosive, then we can turn around and march right back out the gate."

"There doesn't seem to be any place handy, Max."

"Don't worry. We'll find—"

A second group of young men came pouring out of the administration building. They were led by a young man with a crew-cut and an exceptionally serious-looking expression. Suddenly spotting Max and 99 he halted the group, then approached them.

"I'm Frank Sadwell," he said, glowering. "I'm the senior freshman. Aren't you two freshmen, too?"

Max introduced himself and 99 using their assumed names. "We were just on the way to the administration building to plant a . . . that is, to register," Max said.

"You can do that later," Sadwell snapped. "Right now, all freshmen are due at the auditorium. We're to hear The Professor's welcoming address."

"Yes, that's what I said, we were on our way to the auditorium to hear The Professor's welcoming address," Max said.

"Fall in!" Frank Sadwell barked.

Max and 99 joined the group, then Sadwell marched it off toward the auditorium.

"We'll probably find some place along the way to plant the explosive," Max said to 99.

"Careful, Max. That Frank Sadwell is watching you. I think he's suspicious."

"Impossible," Max said. "Our cover identities are perfect."

Sadwell dropped back to the rear of the formation, alongside Max and 99. "Have we met before?" he said suspiciously to Max. "You look familiar to me."

"Do you spend much time in Miami Beach?" Max asked.

"Never been there."

"Then maybe that's it," Max said. "I haven't either."

"It's your face," Sadwell said, his eyes narrowing. "Somewhere, I've seen it before."

"It must have been right where it is now," Max replied. "It doesn't move around much."

"A picture. I think I've seen a picture of you."

"In my high school class year book, maybe?"

"I don't read year books," Sadwell replied curtly. "My reading is limited to 'Wanted' posters. I try to keep up on the identities of all the Control agents. That's how I got into this school. I got a scholarship for superior 'Wanted' poster knowledge."

"Well, you couldn't have seen my picture on a 'Wanted' poster," Max pointed out. "If I were a Control agent, what would I be doing at a KAOS school? Control has a training school of its own, you know. Simple loyalty to the organization would demand that I take my training there."

Sadwell thought about that for a moment, then, without commenting, he moved back to the head of the formation.

"Max, I don't think he was convinced," 99 said.

"Of course he was. Simple logic does it every time. His doubts have been completely laid to rest."

"If you say so, Max."

They marched into the auditorium, then, at Sadwell's command they seated themselves.

A moment later, a crotchety-looking old man hobbled out onto the stage. He peered over his spectacles at the freshmen. Then he spoke. "My name, as you probably know, is Professor," he said. "My first name is The. But, you may call me The Professor. While you are here at the KAOS training school, I will be father, mother, brother, sister, aunt, uncle, cousin and nephew to you. And if you step out of line, I will treat you just like a father, mother, brother, sister, aunt, uncle, cousin or nephew would do. I will spank you soundly and send you to bed without dessert."

There were cheers—and a few tears—from the freshmen.

"Are there any questions?" The Professor asked.

A freshman rose. "What's for dessert tonight?" he queried.

"You'll never know, young man," The Professor replied. "For questioning me, you will be sent to bed without dessert. Now, are there any more questions?"

There were no more questions.

"You're a bright group," The Professor smiled. "A group that asks no questions is obviously a group that knows all the answers. Now," he continued, "we will leave the auditorium and I will take you on a tour of the classrooms."

The Professor hobbled down off the stage, then hobbled toward the doorway.

Frank Sadwell called the group to attention. Then he marched the freshmen off behind The Professor.

"99, look for a place to plant the explosive," Max whispered.

"Max, there just isn't any place out here on the grounds. We'll have to wait until we get inside."

Max sighed. "That means we'll have to listen to a stuffy lecture."

"Maybe we'll be lucky, Max. Maybe we'll find a place to plant the explosive before we get to the classroom."

With The Professor still hobbling along in front, the freshmen entered another building.

"Max! Look!" 99 said. "Up ahead. There's a table. And on the table is a bowl of flowers."

"Yes. Very nice," Max replied. "Daisies, aren't they?"

"What I mean is, Max, you can drop the explosive into the vase."

"Good thinking, 99."

As the group approached the table, Max reached into the black satchel and got out a pellet.

At that very moment, however, The Professor came abreast of the table. "Halt!" he croaked.

The group stopped.

"Goldenrod!" The Professor raged, indicating the flowers in the vase. "Goldenrod is terrible for my hay fever!"

Frank Sadwell rushed up, lifted the vase from the table, then smashed it on the floor. "Frank Sadwell, senior freshman, at your service, sir!" he saluted.

The Professor smiled toothily. "I like you, Sadwell," he said. "You smash a nice vase."

Sadwell saluted again. "My only desire is to serve you faithfully, sir!"

"From now on," The Professor said, "you can call me 'The'."

Once more, Sadwell saluted. Then, with The Professor still in the lead, the group proceeded.

"Too bad, Max," 99 sympathized.

"Yes," Max scowled. "I hate to be mistaken like that. I was *positive* those were daisies."

"Max! Look!"

"Again, 99?"

"Up ahead, Max. There's a rubber tree. See—planted in that wooden tub. You can drop the pellet into the tub!"

"Good thinking, 99!"

As they approached the rubber tree, Max palmed the pellet, preparing to drop it into the tub.

But, at that moment, The Professor cried, "Halt!"

The group pulled up.

"Goldenrod!" The Professor raged, indicating the rubber plant. "Goldenrod is terrible for my hay fever!"

Frank Sadwell, rushed up, hefted the tub above his head, then dropped it to the floor, smashing it to splinters.

The Professor smiled toothily. "What I said before goes double, Sadwell," he said. "Except that now you can call me 'T.P.'."

"Thanks, T.P.," Sadwell grimaced.

"Forward!" The Professor croaked.

"Too bad again, Max," 99 said.

"Too bad? 99, don't you realize what this means? I've been vindicated. If The Professor doesn't know a rubber tree from a goldenrod, then he surely doesn't know a goldenrod from a daisy. I was right the first time."

"But, Max, you haven't planted the pea."

"There are times, 99, when a man would rather be right than a pea planter."

A few seconds later, The Professor led the freshmen into a large classroom. A class was in session. But the instructor gladly turned the floor over to The Professor.

"This is our advanced weapons class," The Professor said to the freshmen. "That doesn't mean that the class is advanced. As a matter of fact, the class is behind. It's the weapons that are advanced. Is that clear?"

"Perfectly clear," Max replied.

"No dessert for you tonight," The Professor snapped. "A good freshman speaks only when spoken to." He addressed the group again. "The weapons you see in this classroom," he said, "are the weapons that are available to KAOS agents for combating Control agents. Each model represents a new scientific advancement. The weapons are sent to us by KAOS's Research & Development Department. And, after I have modified the weapons, they are used by the students for training. Are there any questions?"

The freshmen remained silent.

"There must be a question," The Professor insisted. "I'll bet not one of you knows what 'modified' means. Who knows what it means?"

Not one hand went up.

"Then why don't you ask questions!" The Professor raged.

Max put up his hand. "I have a question, sir."

"Hah! Caught you!" The Professor grinned craftily. "For that, you'll go without dessert tonight. Didn't I tell you—no questions!"

"You took away my tonight's dessert before," Max pointed out.

"Don't be a nit-picker," The Professor said. "Nobody likes a nit-picker. And, just to show you what a warm, kind, compassionate human being I am, I'll let you have your dessert tonight and I'll also answer your question. 'Modified' means changed."

"Does that mean, sir," Frank Sadwell said, "that after R & D develops these scientific weapons, you change them?"

The Professor smiled upon him. "I like a boy that asks questions," he said. "Yes, that's what it means. The fact is, R & D ruins these weapons with a lot of new-fangled gimcracks. They're not dependable. It's my job, as I see it, to build Dependability into them, after R & D leaves it out. Does that answer your question?"

"Perfectly, sir," Frank Sadwell replied unhappily.

"You're a jewel, lad," The Professor smiled. Once more he addressed the entire group. "I'm going to demonstrate some of these weapons," he said, grinning mischievously. "And I'll need a volunteer, someone to take the part of the Control agent, the victim. Who could pretend to be a Control agent?"

The freshmen stood still and silent.

"It won't hurt," The Professor cackled impishly.

Frank Sadwell took a step backwards.

"Not you, dear boy," The Professor said. "I wouldn't want to hurt you."

"I stepped backwards, sir. That's tantamount to declining the invitation twice."

"Good thinking, boy. This could be dangerous." Again, he spoke to the group. "Come now—a volunteer."

Frank Sadwell stepped sideways, placing himself directly behind Max.

"Surely, one of you could pretend, just for a few minutes, to be a Control agent," The Professor urged.

Pushed from behind, Max stumbled forward.

"Oh, you think you could be a Control agent, do you?" The Professor said suspiciously. "Frankly, I consider that a little suspicious. No KAOS freshman who was worth his salt would ever want to be a Control agent—not even make-believe."

"I was pushed," Max explained.

The Professor waggled a finger at the group. "Our volunteer has just illustrated a very important point," he said. "Never believe anything a Control agent says. I've never seen it to fail. When a Control agent volunteers, every time, he'll claim he was pushed." He peered past Max at Frank Sadwell. "Isn't that right, boy?"

"The dirty dogs," Frank Sadwell replied grimly in agreement.

7.

"THE IMPORTANT thing is, now we have a victim, some-one to take the part of the enemy agent," The Professor said. He looked Max up and down. "You look a little familiar," he said. "Haven't I seen you somewhere before?"

"Yes, sir. You've seen me right here," Max replied. "And, every time, you've taken away my dessert."

"If you're that kind of student, you deserve everything that's coming to you." He stepped to the instructor's desk and picked up a weapon, a pistol. "This—" he began.

But at that moment a senior stepped into the room, and all of the freshmen snapped to attention, inter-rupting.

The senior began making the rounds with his hand out. "Sorry, sir," he said to The Professor. "Just collec-ting for the Senior Fun."

"Perfectly all right," The Professor smiled. "Tradition is more important than education. And don't forget my ten per cent cut."

As soon as the senior had finished making the collection, he saluted The Professor, slipped him his ten per cent cut, then departed.

"And that concludes our lesson on weapons," The Professor said to the class.

Frank Sadwell stepped forward. "Excuse me, sir," he said. "But you haven't demonstrated the weapons yet."

The Professor looked surprised. "I haven't? Are you sure?"

Sadwell indicated Max. "The enemy agent is still alive," he pointed out.

"Snitch!" Max hissed.

"By Harry, you're right," The Professor said. "There he is, standing there, straight as a beanstalk. That couldn't be—not if I'd demonstrated the weapons. Well . . . we'll remedy that." He picked up the pistol again. "This little item was sent to us just recently by R & D," he said. "It's an electronic pistol. And, according to R & D, when fired, it paralyzes the enemy by freezing his brain cells."

There was applause from the freshmen.

"You're out of order!" The Professor snapped. "That's the most ridiculous thing I ever heard of—a pistol that freezes a man's brain cells!"

The freshmen booed.

"That's better," The Professor smiled. "We don't want to encourage those featherheads at R & D. *I* don't want to, anyway. That's why I've modified this pistol. I took out all those little doohingies they had inside it, and I put in some good old-fashioned dependability."

There were cheers again.

"I will now demonstrate," The Professor said, facing toward Max. He aimed the pistol directly at him.

"Are you sure it's harmless?" Max said worriedly.

"What kind of a weapon would it be if it were harmless?" The Professor growled. "You sound like those featherheads at R & D."

"But, have you considered the consequences?" Max said. "If that pistol isn't harmless, you may lose a freshman."

"Our classes are too large anyway," The Professor replied. "This is one way of whittling them down to size." Again, he aimed the pistol.

But at that moment another senior entered the room. The freshmen snapped to attention. And Max snapped to attention and ducked.

"Excuse me, sir," the senior said to The Professor. "Just collecting for the Senior Fun."

"Proceed," The Professor smiled. "On the usual terms, of course."

"Of course, sir—your ten per cent."

The senior began collecting. When he reached Max, Max gave him a nickel.

"Cheap!" the senior snarled.

"That's my last cent," Max explained.

"You won't need money where you're going," The Professor said comfortingly.

The senior, having finished the collection, handed The Professor his cut, then departed.

"Now then, on to the next classroom," The Professor said.

Once more, Frank Sadwell stepped forward. "Just a reminder, sir," he said. "You haven't demonstrated the weapons yet."

The Professor scowled. "Are you—"

Frank Sadwell interrupted, pointing to Max.

"By Harry!" The Professor muttered. "Well, on with the demonstration." He aimed the pistol squarely at Max's head and pulled the trigger.

A boxing glove popped from the end of the barrel and caught Max right between the eyes. Max dropped to the floor.

99 rushed forward. "Max! Are you all right!" She bent down to him.

"He's fine. Unconscious is all," The Professor said. "Surely you don't think I would knock him off this soon! I need him for further demonstration." He addressed the group again. "Now *that* is dependability," he said. "R & D can keep it's new-fangled gadgets. When you're up against the wily enemy, what you want is a good old-fashioned pistol that fires a boxing glove out the barrel and pops the adversary right between the eyes. Can't beat it for dependability. The old weapons are the best weapons. Remember that!"

Aided by 99, Max sat up, regaining consciousness.

"Max! Are you all right?" 99 fretted.

Max shook his head, trying to clear it. "My brain cells are a little chilly," he said. "But, otherwise, I feel awful."

"On your feet, make-believe Control agent!" The Professor commanded. "This is no time to lounge. I have other weapons to demonstrate."

"Maybe someone else would like to volunteer," Max said, rising. "I don't want to hog all the glory."

The Professor turned to the group. "Would someone else like to volunteer?"

There was no response.

"Come, come," The Professor urged. "Who else will volunteer?"

Frank Sadwell stepped forward. As he did, he gave Max a second shove.

"Well, all right," The Professor said to Max. "If you want to hog all the glory, it's fine by me. After all, it's your funeral."

"He was *pushed!*" 99 protested.

"That's a serious accusation," The Professor frowned. "Who pushed him?"

99 pointed at Frank Sadwell. "He did! I saw it!"

"Ha! Watching the other students while you're supposed to be paying attention to my lecture, eh!" The Professor growled. "For that, you lose your dessert.

Now, on with the demonstration." He walked to the desk. "Over here, victim," he said to Max. He indicated a large metal box that was sitting on the desk. "According to R & D," he said. "This machine is a laser-powered lie-detector. Ever heard anything funnier than that?"

The freshmen roared with laughter.

"Naturally, I had to modify it," The Professor said.

Max put a hand in front of his face.

"It doesn't fire a boxing glove," The Professor said.

"Oh." Max lowered the hand.

"Stand right here, right beside the machine," The Professor ordered.

Max obeyed.

"The way those featherheads at R & D had this worked out," The Professor said to the group, "whenever a question was asked, and a lie was answered, a little light went on and a bell rang. Obviously, it was undependable that way. What do lights and bells know about truth? As modified, however, the machine is one-hundred per cent effective. I'll prove it." He faced back to Max. "I'll ask you a question," he said. "You can answer it with the truth or a lie, it won't make any difference."

"Is there any *other* choice?" Max asked.

"It still wouldn't make any difference," The Professor replied. "Now, here's your first question. If there are fourteen apples in a dozen, and you bake twelve of the apples into a cherry pie, how long is a piece of string?"

Max puzzled for a moment. "A long piece of string or a short piece of string?"

"It doesn't make any difference," The Professor replied. "What is your answer?"

"A peach pie," Max replied.

The instant he answered, a rubber hose popped from the machine and began beating him about the head and shoulders. Max leaped out of range, but not before he had been severely clubbed.

"See? I told you it didn't make any difference," The Professor smiled. "Lying or telling the truth, that rubber hose beats the stuffing out of you. It's fool-proof!"

"It's certainly more effective than lights and bells," Max agreed.

"Oh, you're not convinced, eh?" The Professor said. "All right, we'll try another question. Take your place beside the machine."

"I'm convinced," Max protested.

"You say that, but you don't really mean it," The Professor replied. "I can see it in your eyes. You doubt the value of my modification. In fact, pretending to be a Control agent, you think you can beat the machine. Don't you?"

Max smiled. "Well, I think we ought to realize that there *are* some very clever Control agents. I have one in particular in mind. You may have heard of him. Max Smart is his name. As I understand it, he is Control's top agent, and, when it comes to brains, a whiz kid to boot."

"I accept that challenge," The Professor said. "Make believe you are this Jack Sharp."

"Max Smart. M-a-x S-m-a-r-t."

Frank Sadwell stepped forward. "This freshman is correct, sir," he said to The Professor. "Jack Sharp is Control's top agent—according to the notation on the back of his 'Wanted' poster."

"Max Smart," Max said.

"Oh, you keep up on 'Wanted' posters, eh?" The Professor said approvingly. "Would you know this Sax Heart if you saw him?"

"Max Smart," Max said.

"His image is etched in my brain," Frank Sadwell replied. "I would recognize him anywhere, under any conditions."

"Very good," The Professor smiled. "That's the kind of students we need at KAOS." He turned back to Max.

"All right, we shall proceed. Stand beside the machine, and pretend that you are Max Smart."

"Jack Sharp," Max corrected, stepping to the machine.

"Here is your question," The Professor said. "If beetles are bugs, and the Beatles are boys, how many boy beetles does it take to bug a Beatle boy until he boils?"

Max smiled smugly. "My answer," he replied, "is 'yes and no.' "

The machine chugged, clanked, then fell silent. The rubber hose did not appear.

"Traitor!" The Professor shrieked at the machine.

"I think it lost its cool," Max smiled.

The Professor snatched up the pistol, aimed at the machine, and fired. The boxing glove popped out of the barrel and struck the machine square between the dials. The machine chugged again. Then the rubber hose popped out and began beating Max about the head and shoulders.

Max, stunned, dropped to the floor.

"Max!" 99 cried, rushing to him.

"Can't beat old-fashioned dependability," The Professor cackled. To the group, he said, "Take five. Then, after recess, I'll demonstrate the rest of these weapons. I think you'll be particularly interested in our new white corpuscle destroying machine. It has an intriguing boxing glove attachment. Dismissed!"

The freshmen straggled out, followed by The Professor.

"Max! Wake up!" 99 pleaded, patting Max's face.

Max stirred. "What's the next question?" he said fuzzily.

"Are you all right, Max?"

"I don't think I know the answer to that. Do you have an easier one?"

At that moment, Frank Sadwell returned to the room.

He was carrying a pail of water. "The Professor asked me to revive him," he explained to 99. "He wants him to be in shape for the next demonstration."

"I'm revived," Max said.

Frank Sadwell threw the water into his face.

"Why did you do that?" Max asked, annoyed and dripping.

"I always follow orders," Frank Sadwell replied. "The Professor said, 'Throw some water in his face and revive him.' "

"But, I told you, I was already revived."

"That only covered the 'revived,' that didn't cover the 'water,' " Frank Sadwell said. "You should have said, 'I'm already revived, and you don't have to throw water in my face.' How was I to know?"

"My apologies," Max muttered.

"Outside," Frank said to Max and 99. "The Professor wants you to get some fresh air so you'll be in shape for the next demonstration."

"Couldn't we stay in here?" Max asked.

"The Professor wants—"

"I know, I know—outside."

Max and 99 left the room, followed by Frank Sadwell. When they got outside, Frank moved on, and joined The Professor, who, a short distance away, was talking informally to a number of the freshmen.

"Max, how are we going to plant the explosive?" 99 said worriedly. "There isn't any place out here to drop it."

"99, I think the time has come to make a policy decision," Max said.

"Yes, Max?"

"The question is, which is more important, planting that explosive or saving the life of Jack Sharp?"

"Who, Max?"

"Sorry. That beating mixed me up a bit. Max Smart, I meant to say."

"I don't think I understand, Max."

"99, the only way we can plant that explosive is to return to the classroom. But, if we return to the classroom, The Professor will continue to use me to demonstrate the KAOS weapons. And, frankly, 99, I don't think I'll survive. Now, do you understand?"

"I think so, Max. But what's the answer?"

Max threw up his arms, covering his head.

"I'm not the lie-detector, Max. I won't hit you," 99 said.

"Instinct," Max explained. "From now on, whenever I hear that question, 'What is the answer,' I'm going to duck."

"Then, what can we do? Is that better, Max?"

"Yes, but it doesn't answer the question. Which is more important, 99? Planting the explosive, or my life?"

"Max, that's easy. Your life is more important."

"I tend to agree with you on that, 99."

"But, on the other hand, planting the explosive is very important, too."

"Yes, it's a difficult decision to make."

"It's your life, Max."

"That makes it easier," Max said. "Let's run."

"We better not run, Max," 99 said. "That might create suspicion. Let's just walk."

"99, this is *my* life. I say let's run!"

"Let's compromise, Max. Let's trot."

"That's fair."

Having reached the decision, Max and 99 trotted toward the gate.

"After we escape," 99 said, "maybe we could drop the pellet on the school grounds from the helicopter. We *might* hit it, you know."

"99, we couldn't even hit the school grounds with two bodies," Max said. "We tried it, remember? When we parachuted."

"Well, we could *try*, Max."

Max halted. "It's no use," he said. "Duty first. I can't leave, 99, until after I've planted that explosive. Even if it costs me my life. We'll have to go back."

"Max . . . you'll be in tremendous danger!"

"Yes," Max replied grimly, "and hating every second of it."

"But, if that's what you want, Max. . . ."

"Attenshun!" a voice barked.

Max and 99 found themselves facing a senior.

"Cough up," the senior commanded.

Max turned his pockets inside-out. "You're out of luck, fella," he said. "Every cent I had is in the Fun already."

"We'll take anything of value," the senior said. "What do you have in the black bag?"

"A change of shirts," Max replied.

"Let's see."

"I don't want to waste your time," Max said. "If you've seen one change of shirts, you've seen them all."

"I'll chance it," the senior said, taking the bag from Max and opening it. He frowned. "These aren't shirts."

"I must have picked up the wrong black satchel when I left home," Max said.

The senior took out the packet of explosives. "What are these green gumdrops?" he said. "I've never seen green gumdrops shaped like this before. They look like peas."

"It's a new gimmick to keep children from eating gumdrops," Max replied. "They think they're peas and won't touch them."

"I'll take a handful," the senior smiled, taking a handful. "I'll put them in the Senior Fun. With these gumdrops on hand, we won't need money. That's what we spend the money on, anyway, when we go into town —gumdrops." He dropped the remaining pellets back into the bag. "I'll stop you later and get the rest of them," he said. "I don't like to be greedy all at once."

"The world could use more seniors like you," Max said.

"Dismissed!" the senior barked. And he strolled away.

"All right, 99," Max said. "Back to the classroom."

"Max! No! We don't have to now!"

"I'm afraid we do, 99. The decision has been made."

"But, Max," 99 said, tugging at him. "The explosive has been planted. Our mission has been completed!"

"Pardon, 99?"

"Those pellets, Max! That senior will put them in the Senior Fun. They're planted!"

Max frowned thoughtfully. "It seems too easy."

"But it's true, Max. Now we can escape. You don't have to sacrifice your life."

Max looked a little disappointed. "I was getting used to the idea," he said. "I thought I might even get a medal." He shrugged. "Ah, well, easy come, easy go. Let's go, 99."

Once more, Max and 99 trotted toward the gate. A few moments later, reaching it, they were stopped by the sentry.

"Identification," he ordered.

Max and 99 produced the identification papers they had taken from the real students.

"Now there's a coincidence for you," the sentry said. "Macy and Gimbel. It was only about an hour ago that another pair with those names came in here. And now, here you two are, leaving. It's a small world."

"I'll bet a lot of interesting things happen to you, out here on guard duty," Max said.

"Would you believe it?" the guard replied. "Just this morning, I saw two people jump out of a helicopter."

"That's a *lit-tle* hard to believe," Max smiled.

"Suppose I told you they were wearing parachutes?"

"A bit far-fetched," Max replied.

"And thumbing through a sheaf of papers on the way down?"

"You're pulling my leg," Max said.

"You're too sharp for me," the sentry grinned. "But you'd be surprised at the number of people who would believe a story like that." He saluted. "Have a fun time in town," he said. "Don't eat too many gumdrops."

Max and 99 sauntered on.

When they got out of sight of the gate, they left the the road and entered the underbrush. Macy and Gimbel were still where they had left them, still bound and gagged. Max and 99 released them.

"Did we pass the initiation?" Macy grinned.

"With flying colors," Max replied. "Now, you're free to go on to the school and take up your studies. In fact, you're expected in The Professor's class. He's conducting a lecture on modern weapons systems."

"You better hurry," 99 said.

Macy and Gimbel darted off through the underbrush.

"A word of advice!" Max called after them. "Don't volunteer for anything!"

But they were out of earshot.

Max and 99 returned to the road. The helicopter was hovering overhead. Max signalled to Lance Chalfont, and the helicopter began descending.

"This is certainly going to be a banner day for that sentry," Max smiled. "Imagine! Three sets of Macys and Gimbels in one morning!"

8.

As SOON as Max and 99 were safely back aboard the helicopter, Max got out the fact sheet on their next destination, the KAOS Old Agents Home.

"It's in Minnesota," Max said to Lance Chalfont. "Can you find Minnesota?"

"Is it anywhere near Minniehaha?" he asked.

"Not far from there," Max replied. "If you can find Minniehaha, you can find Minnesota."

"Shouldn't we report in to the Chief, Max?" 99 said.

"Good thinking," Max replied, taking off his shoe and dialing.

Chief: Is that you, Max?

Max: Yes, this is me, Operator. Connect me with the Chief, please.

Chief: Max, this *is* me.

Max: Oh, sorry, Chief. I'm so used to dialing you and getting the Operator instead that I expect it to happen as a matter of course.

Operator: Are you saying I'm some kind of a but-tinski?

Max: Not exactly, Operator. What I meant was—

Operator: Nobody can say I'm a buttinski. When did I ever butt in on anybody's private conversation?

Max: Operator, what I said was—

Operator: You want to get me fired, don't you? I know your kind. You intend to report me to the Super-visor. You'll tell her I'm a buttinski. Is that your plan? Is that the reward I get for serving you faithfully for lo these many years? That's gratitude!

Max: Operator, I have no intention—

Operator: Don't butt in. It's okay for you to butt in, huh? But not me. Oh no, I can't say a word. I'm just supposed to sit here like a lump on a log and let you report me to the Supervisor for butting in and not say a word in my own defense. I guess you never heard of the Bill of Rights. Every man has the right to challenge his accuser. That goes for telephone operators, too. You think William Jennings Bryan didn't have telephone operators in mind when he wrote the Bill of Rights?

Max: William Jennings Bryan?

Operator: Sure. It's named after him. Bill. Bill Bryan.

Max: I apologize, Operator. I'm sorry I called you a buttinski. Now, am I forgiven? May I speak to the Chief?

Operator: I think he's out to lunch.

Chief: I'm not out to lunch, Operator. I'm right here.

Operator: Don't butt in.

Max: Chief, try to ignore her.

Operator: Just for that, I won't say another word.

Max: Fine. Now, Chief—

Operator: I'm a human being, too, you know. I have feelings. What do you think I am, a recorded announce-ment? I have feelings just like anybody. In fact, I'm very sensitive. My psychiatrist says I'm *too* sensitive. "You're too sensitive, Operator," he keeps telling me. "You let little things bother you," he says. "Well, you would, too,"

I tell him, "if you had to put up with this one guy. He won't take care of his shoe." So my psychiatrist says—

Max: Operator, shut up!

Operator: That's what my psychiatrist says. How did you know?

Max: It was a wild guess. Now, please, be quiet for a minute and let me talk to the Chief. I have an important report to make.

(Silence)

Max: Operator? Are you there? Are you going to keep quiet?

(Silence)

Max: Operator, I'm sorry if I hurt your feelings.

Operator: I'm not speaking to you.

Chief: Max, this is your chance. Give me your report.

Max: Chief, I can't. Not while the Operator is pouting. I just wouldn't feel right about it. Operator? Speak to me.

Operator: Your party does not answer, sir.

Max: Oh, all right, if you want to be that way about it. Chief? Still there?

Chief: Give me your report, Max.

Operator: Coax me, Max.

Max: Here's the way things stand, Chief. We have successfully planted the explosive inside KAOS's training school and we are now proceeding toward our next objective, KAOS's Old Agents Home. Do you have any word of the opposition?

Operator: Just a word from you, Max, and all will be forgiven.

Chief: I think I have good news, Max. Your decision to skip lunch was apparently a master stroke. The KAOS agent has not yet been observed at Control's Old Agents Home. So, evidently, the race is neck and neck again.

Operator: Chief, you talk to him. Try to get him to make up.

Max: That *is* good news, Chief. I have full confidence now that we will win out in this race against the forces of evil.

Operator: Max . . . I'll do something desperate!

Chief: There's one thing, Max . . . It's bad news. I was saving it for last.

Operator: I'll stub my toe, Max. And I'll reject all medical attention. And gangrene will set in.

Max: I think I can take it, Chief. What is the bad news?

Operator (frantic)*:* Maxie, Maxie, speak to me!

Chief: We have intercepted a coded message from KAOS headquarters, Max. It seems that KAOS has discovered that you are being transported on your mission by helicopter. And—

Operator: Last chance, Max! Speak to me!

Max: How did KAOS discover that fact, Chief?

Chief: KAOS decoded one of our coded messages, Max. And, the upshot is that KAOS has sent its air force to intercept you.

Operator: I'll stick my head in a glass of water and drown myself, Max! Honest!

Max: I'm not too worried about that, Chief. After all, we have Lance Chalfont, silent birdman, piloting our plane.

Operator: Lance . . . are you there? Tell Max to speak to me! Tell him if he doesn't, I'll do something terrible. Tell him I'll plug myself into the switchboard and electrocute myself!

Chief: Well, I wish I could be of help, Max. But all I can do is tell you to watch out for those KAOS interceptors.

Max: Don't worry, Chief. I'm sure that Lance Chalfont can handle the situation. I'll report in again when I have something to report in.

Chief: Good luck, Max.

Max: All right now, Operator. What were you saying?
Operator (indignantly): I'm not speaking to you!
(Click!)

Max hung up his shoe.

"What is it, Max?" 99 said.

"Bad, 99."

"But what is it?"

"The Operator isn't speaking to me any more."

"Oh."

"Did I hear you speak my name during that conversation?" Lance Chalfont said to Max.

"Yes, you did, Lance," Max replied. "That's the other bad news. The Chief advised me that KAOS has sent its air force to intercept us. But I told him that I wasn't worried—because we have Lance Chalfont, silent birdman, as our pilot. I was sure that you would know how to handle the situation."

"Bail out!" Lance Chalfont screamed. "Hit the silk!"

"Isn't that a little loud for a silent birdman?" Max commented.

"I panic easy," Lance Chalfont replied, regaining his calm. "But it don't last. Once that first panic is passed, I get like a rock."

"Strong and sturdy, you mean."

"No, I mean I can't swim. I sink like a rock. Say," he said, "did the Chief say what them KAOS interceptors looked like?"

"No, he didn't mention that."

"I wonder if they look like a bunch of swoopin' birds," Lance Chalfont said.

"Possibly. Why do you ask?"

Lance Chalfont pointed out the front window. "Up there! Don't that look like a bunch of swoopin' birds?"

Max and 99 looked.

"It's them!" Max cried.

"Bail out!" Lance Chalfont screamed. "Quick, hit the silk!"

"They're diving on us!" 99 shouted.

"That's funny," Max mused. "They're not getting any larger. Wouldn't you think that—"

"False alarm," Lance Chalfont broke in. "It's nothin' but a bunch of swoopin' birds."

The birds swooped by.

Max looked around the plane. "What do we have to defend ourselves with?" he said.

"Look in that tin box back there," Lance Chalfont said. "You'll find a jar of bread crumbs."

"Bread crumbs?"

"Best defense there is against swoopin' birds," Lance Chalfont replied. "They leave the plane alone and go after the bread crumbs."

"I had in mind defending ourselves against the KAOS interceptors," Max explained.

"In a case like that, you dump out the bread crumbs and throw the jar," Lance Chalfont replied.

"Max," 99 said, "maybe there's something in the black bag that we can use. Surely, R & D sent along some sort of a weapon."

"I think I'll check the black bag," Max replied. "It's just possible that R & D sent along some sort of a weapon."

"Good thinking, Max."

Max opened the black bag. The first item he took from it looked like a cigarette holder.

"That's odd," Max said.

"What, Max?"

"This cigarette holder has a trigger on it. Oh . . . here, I see. Actually, it's a 20 mm. cannon."

"It isn't big enough to be a 20 mm. cannon, Max."

"It's a miniature 20 mm. cannon."

"Oh. That makes sense."

"This is the answer," Max said. "When those KAOS interceptors show up, we'll knock them right out of the sky with this 20 mm. cannon."

"Is it loaded, Max?"

"If it's loaded," Max added.

"You better try it just to make sure," 99 said.

"I'll try it just to make sure," Max nodded, pointing the cigarette holder out the open doorway. He pulled the trigger.

Just as Max fired the cannon, Lance Chalfont turned in his seat to watch. But he forgot to loosen his grip on the steering mechanism. Consequently, the helicopter tipped on its side, and the cannon shell shot straight up into the air.

"I see it!" 99 cried, looking up.

"Up, up, up!" Max commented approvingly.

"Yup," Lance Chalfont said. "And now it's spent and it's turnin' around and comin' down, down, down."

"That proves that the cannon is loaded," Max said. "We're all set to meet those KAOS interceptors."

At that instant there was a crashing sound.

"Was that anything we should worry about?" Max asked Lance Chalfont.

"I guess a little frettin' wouldn't do no harm," Lance Chalfont replied. "That cannon shell just passed through our gas tank." He pointed. "If you look at it from just the right angle, you can see the gasoline pourin' out of the tank."

Max looked. "Ummmm, yes. That is interesting—considering that this is an atom-powered helicopter. Lucky for us it's nothing to worry about."

"I guess it just wouldn't do no harm to worry a little bit, too, on top of the frettin'," Lance Chalfont said. "When all that gasoline runs out, the engine is gonna stop. And when the engine stops, we're gonna fall right out of the sky."

Max looked at him puzzledly. "But this is an atom-powered helicopter," he said.

"What do you think them atoms run on, man? Gasoline!"

"Hadn't we better land?" 99 said.

"I'll look in the manual," Lance Chalfont replied, reaching for a booklet that was hanging by a string to one of the control knobs. "It don't do to panic in a situation like this. The thing to do is check the manual. It says so right in the manual."

The engine began sputtering, and the helicopter began gradually descending.

Calmly, Lance Chalfont paged through the manual.

"Hurry!" 99 urged.

"I'm not sure what to look it up under," Lance Chalfont replied. "I can't find no heading for 'What to do when somebody fires a 20 mm. cannon out the doorway and the shell goes up instead of out and then comes down and blasts a hole right through the gas tank.' "

"Look under 'W' for 'What'," Max suggested.

"Oh, yeah, here it is!"

"What does it say!" 99 cried.

"It says, 'Land!' "

At that instant, the helicopter bumped to a spine-jarring landing.

"Lucky we had the manual," Lance Chalfont smiled. "Otherwise, we'd've never made it."

Max looked out the doorway. "Apparently we landed in a jungle," he said. "That means that we're miles and miles from civilization. It also means that we will be unable to repair the helicopter and complete our mission. In other words, we have failed. Control is doomed!"

"Look on the bright side," Lance Chalfont said. "The bread crumbs wasn't harmed. We won't have to worry about no swoopin' birds."

Max stared gloomily at the thick foliage surrounding

the plane. "Lost in the vast wastes of Nowhere!" he groaned.

99 cocked her head. "Max . . . don't I hear voices?"

Max listened. "As a matter of fact . . ."

At that moment, an African stepped out of the jungle. He was accompanied by a woman and three small children. They were dressed in casual wear.

"Saved!" 99 cried.

"Hold on there," Lance Chalfont said. "These may be some of them six-foot pygmies. Better let me handle this. I got experience." He stepped from the helicopter and approached the Africans. "We tumble out sky in great silver bird," he said. "You savvy?"

The woman and the children looked at the helicopter curiously. And the man addressed Lance Chalfont. "Are you talking about that red helicopter?" he asked.

"Rightum. Red helicopter, great silver bird. What place this?"

"You're in luck," the man replied. "You landed in Burundi National Park. Did your engine conk out?"

"Great silver bird lose-um gasoline," Lance Chalfont replied.

The man looked puzzled. "Really? Isn't that one of the new atom-powered models?"

"What-um you think-um atoms run on? Gasoline!"

"Well, I have an extra container of gasoline in my car," the man said. "You may have it."

At that moment, Max stepped forward. "We appreciate that," he said. "But we also have another problem. Our gas tank has two holes in it."

The man looked past him at the helicopter. "20 mm. shells?" he guessed.

"Exactly," Max replied. "Now, if we—"

"Hold on there," Lance Chalfont broke in. "You can't get nowhere talkin' to this native like that," he said to Max. "You got to speak the lingo. Let me handle it." He addressed the man again. "Is these pygmies safe to have around-um?" he said, indicating the children. "The last time I come up against a bunch-um of pygmies they durn near done me in-um."

"These are the children," the man explained. "My wife and I are taking them on a picnic."

Lance Chalfont turned to Max. "Hear that? Picnic. Food. We're up against a bunch of cannibals, fella. You run back to the plane and get the bread crumbs. Bread crumbs'll distract a cannibal almost as quick as a swoopin' bird."

"You go get the bread crumbs," Max said. "I'll stay here and try to find out if there's a helicopter repair shop anywhere near by."

"Be right back!" Lance Chalfont said, dashing toward the plane.

"No, there isn't a helicopter repair shop near by," the man said to Max as Lance Chalfont departed. "But I have a suggestion. You might plug those holes with coconuts. Naturally, it would be only a temporary solution, but, at least, it would get you back to civilization."

"How far is civilization from here?" Max asked.

"Oh, about a mile and a half. It starts just outside the park."

Lance Chalfont came rushing back. "I got the bread crumbs," he said. "You still in one piece?"

"Why wouldn't I be?" Max asked.

"I thought maybe you might've offered to shake hands and that fella bit it off." He held up the jar of bread crumbs. "Don't that look yummy?" he said to the children.

Shyly, they drew back.

"Thank you, anyway," the woman said to Lance Chalfont. "But I don't want them to spoil their lunch."

"Take cover!" Lance Chalfont cried. "They got us on the menu!" He raced back toward the plane.

"He panics easily," Max explained to the man.

"I think-um him a little bit off-um his nut," the man smiled.

"And speaking of nuts," Max said, "where would I find a coco?"

The man led Max into the jungle and showed him a coconut tree. There were coconuts on the ground, and Max selected two and carried them back to the plane.

Just as Max was completing the job of plugging up the holes in the tank, the man reappeared, carrying an emergency can of gasoline. He emptied it into the tank.

"Good—no leakage," Max smiled. He thanked the man for helping him, then got back aboard the helicopter.

"It's a ghost!" Lance Chalfont shrieked, hiding his head in the tin box that had once held the jar of bread crumbs.

"He thinks you were eaten by the cannibals, Max," 99 explained.

"I'm not a ghost," Max assured Lance Chalfont. "But I will be if those KAOS interceptors find us sitting here on the ground, defenseless. Let's get out of here."

Lance Chalfont straightened up. "How'd you get away from them cannibals?" he asked.

"I simply asked them to help us."

"That's kind of hard to believe," Lance Chalfont replied.

"Would you believe that the cannibal chief was carrying an emergency can of gasoline in his car and that he gave it to us?"

"That's far-fetched as all get out."

"Would you believe, then, that I plugged up the holes in the tank with coconuts?"

"I'd believe it if you told me the whole terrible experience has affected your mind," Lance Chalfont replied.

"All right then, believe that," Max said. "And have

pity on me and get back at the controls and fly this helicopter out of here."

"I guess that'd be the kind thing to do," Lance Chalfont agreed.

He settled in the pilot's seat, started the engine, and took off.

As the helicopter rose, Lance Chalfont smiled, impressed. "Ain't it a marvel what kindness will do?" he said. "It's flyin' this helicopter just like it had gas in it."

"It's better than that," Max said. "It also plugged up the holes with coconuts."

"Sakes alive!" Lance Chalfont said in wonder.

A few hours later, Lance Chalfont pointed out the front window and cried, "Thar she blows!"

"Where?" Max said.

"Right down there! A whale! See it!"

"Oh, yes," Max replied. "But we're looking for Minnesota. I don't think you'll find it in the middle of the ocean."

"Is that the ocean?" Lance Chalfont said, disappointed. "I thought that was one of the Great Lakes."

"How could you make a mistake like that?"

"It's full of water," Lance Chalfont replied. "That's what I go by."

"Then *keep* going," Max said. "You'll know Minnesota when you get to it. It's the second state over from the state that looks like a poodle sitting up on its hind legs and begging."

"Oh, *that* one!"

"Max," 99 said, "when we reach the KAOS Old Agents Home do you have any plan for getting inside?"

"Not as yet," Max replied. "But something will occur to me. Let's take a look at the fact sheet."

99 got a sheaf of papers from the black bag and handed it to him. "We're probably a little young to pose as old agents," she said.

"Yes . . . unless we could convince them that we're in our second childhood."

"I knew a fella once that was in his second childhood," Lance Chalfont said. "He was 99 years old. But he had everybody believin' that he was only 66."

"How did he do it?" Max asked.

"He stood on his head."

"Pardon?"

"Stood on his head," Lance Chalfont replied. "You turn 99 upside down, and it looks like 66."

"I see," Max nodded, turning his attention back to the fact sheet.

"I got a lot of stories like that," Lance Chalfont said. "Ever hear about the fella who was 66 years old and wanted folks to think he was older? Know what he did?"

"Stood on his head?"

Lance Chalfont turned to Max, surprised. "You knew that fella, too, eh?"

"Will you excuse us, please?" Max said. "We want to study the fact sheet.

"Max! Look!" 99 said, peering over Max's shoulder. "On the fact sheet it says that the KAOS Old Agents Home isn't really an old agents home. It's a cover for KAOS's Secret Medical Experiments Hospital."

"Hmmmm," Max hmmmmed, interested. "Unless I miss my guess, it's where KAOS conducts its secret medical experiments. That's quite a coincidence. As you know, 99, Control's Old Agents Home isn't an old agents home either. It's where Control conducts its secret medical experiments."

"I know, Max."

"You know what, 99?"

"That Control's Old Agents Home isn't really—"

"Thar she blows!" Lance Chalfont called out, interrupting.

"What this time?" Max asked.

"That state that looks like a poodle," Lance Chalfont replied. "We'll be over Minniehaha any minute now."

"You mean we'll be over Minnesota any minnie now," Max corrected.

9.

"THE QUESTION now is how to get inside," Max said, as the helicopter hovered over the complex of buildings that was supposed to be KAOS's Old Agents Home, but which was really its hospital for conducting scientific medical experiments.

"Max, I think I have an idea," 99 said. "Why don't we pose as salesmen?"

Max shook his head. "That couldn't possibly work, 99."

"Why not, Max?"

"Because you're a woman. How could you pose as a sales*man?* No one would ever believe it."

"Then how about this, Max? You could pose as a salesman, and I could pose as a sales*woman.*"

Max thought a moment. "That's closer to the mark, 99," he said. "But it still wouldn't work. What would a hospital want with a set of Junior Encyclopedias?"

"Max, salesmen sell other things besides encyclopedias. We could pose as salesmen for a drug manufacturer. In fact, we could say that our explosives are really wonder pills, and that we're giving away free samples. That way, we could get the explosives planted in the hospital."

Max shook his head. "I don't like it, 99."

"Why not, Max?" 99 asked, disappointed.

"Because it's a brilliant idea, that's why. And I'm the senior agent, and I'm supposed to think up the brilliant ideas."

"Max," 99 smiled, "it's really *your* idea. I put it together from things you said. For instance, when you said 'encyclopedia,' that made me think of wonder pill."

"I don't quite get the connection, 99."

"Well, who knows what a wonder pill is? And, if there's something you don't know, where do you go to look it up?"

"Encyclopedia."

"Right, Max. See? It's all *your* idea, not mine."

"And a brilliant idea it is, too—even if I did think of it," Max said. He turned to Lance Chalfont. "Land us on that road that leads to the hospital," he said. "We'll approach it on foot."

"On feet, you mean," Lance Chalfont said. "You go approachin' that hospital on one foot, the both of you, and they'll toss you straight into a padded cell."

"All right, have it your way, we'll approach it on feet. But land, so we can get started. There's no time to waste."

Lance Chalfont landed the plane on the road, and Max and 99 got out, with Max carrying the black satchel.

"Wait right here," Max said. "This won't take long. Since we'll be posing as salesmen, I'm sure they'll be anxious to take our free samples and get rid of us. No one likes to have a salesman hanging around. Especially not after they've loaded up on free samples. They keep expecting to be asked to buy something."

"Suppose somebody comes along?" Lance Chalfont said. "Won't it look a little funny, a helicopter sittin' right here in the middle of the road?"

"Tell them you're out of gas," Max suggested.

"An atom-powered helicopter? Who ever heard of an atom-powered helicopter runnin' on gas?"

"Then tell them you're out of atoms," Max said. He turned to 99. "Are you ready, 99?"

"Ready, Max. Is your foot ready?"

"My foot?"

"To put in the door, Max. A salesman always puts his foot in the door."

"Well, all right, if that's how it's done. I just hope I don't break my telephone. The Operator would be furious."

Max and 99 walked up the road. A few minutes later, they reached the gate. The sentry snapped to attention.

"Good afternoon," Max smiled. "We're—"

"I know who you are, Doctor," the sentry replied. He stepped aside so that they could pass. "The welcoming committee is waiting to welcome you," he replied.

"I don't think you understand," Max said. "We—"

"Here comes the welcoming committee now," the sentry interrupted.

Max and 99 looked toward the hospital building and saw a group of doctors approaching.

"I knew it was bound to happen some day," Max said. "Here come the men in the white coats."

99 whispered to him. "Max, I think they think we're somebody else."

"We are," Max whispered back. "We're salesmen."

"No, Max. I think—"

"Welcome, Doctor!" the leader of the group called. "I am Dr. Medulla, the famous brain doctor." He then introduced his colleagues. "This is Dr. H. Nail, the famous finger doctor . . . and Dr. Stubble, the famous chin doctor . . . and Dr. Ache, the famous ear doctor . . . and Dr. Water, the famous knee doctor . . . and, last and least, our intern, Dr. Foot."

"How do you do," Max nodded. "Now . . . who am I?"

Dr. Medulla laughed heartily. "We all know who you are, Doctor," he said. "At least, we know you by reputation. The finest all-'round surgeon in the world, that's who you are. Although we weren't sure at first."

"Oh?" Max replied.

"When we saw your helicopter land down the road, we were a little suspicious," Dr. Medulla said. "But then we saw the little black bag you were carrying and we knew you were a doctor." He frowned. "Incidentally, why did you park your helicopter down the road?"

"Ah . . . would you believe that it's out of gas?" Max asked.

"An atom-powered helicopter? Hardly."

"Then would you believe that it's out of atoms?"

Dr. Medulla shook his head. "Far-fetched."

"Would you believe, then, that we landed it down the road because it's too noisy to be landed in a Hospital Zone?"

"Well, if we had any patients here that would make sense," Dr. Medulla replied.

"You have no patients?"

"Only you-know-who," Dr. Medulla smiled.

"I do? Who do I know who?"

"You know who you know who," Dr. Medulla grinned. He indicated 99. "I see you brought your nurse with you," he said. "That was wise. Our nurses might not be able to assist you. They're very fine nurses, of course. But they aren't familiar with the techniques you employ."

"No, they probably aren't," Max replied.

"Well, shall we go inside?" Dr. Medulla said. "You would probably like to meet the patient."

"You-know-who?"

"Of course I know who. We all know who."

The whole group, including Max and 99, walked toward the main building.

"Dr. Medulla, I have a confession to make," Max said.

"Yes?"

Well, you know how we brilliant doctors are . . . a little absent-minded sometimes."

"Indeed I do," Dr. Medulla replied. "In fact, I practice absent-mindedness every morning for a half-hour. I hope to be a brilliant doctor myself some day."

"Yes. Well, you'll understand then how it is that I don't seem to recall why I'm here."

"Perfectly understandable," Dr. Medulla nodded. "It's the ultimate proof of how brilliant you are. We run-of-the-mill doctors always know why we're where we are." He lowered his voice, speaking to Max confidentially. "But I'm improving," he said. "Last week, I forgot completely that I'm a brain doctor. I took out two livers, a half-dozen spleens and an appendix before I remembered. That's progress, eh?"

"Obviously, you have the makings of a great doctor," Max replied. "But, at the moment, that's no help to me. Perhaps you could tell me—why am I here?"

"To conduct our latest experimental operation."

"Oh, yes, I think it's all coming back to me. Now, if you'll just fill in a few details . . ."

"Well, you know about the human robot that R & D developed."

"Of course I know about the human robot that R & D developed. Tell me about it."

"Well, to make a long story short, R & D has developed a human robot," Dr. Medulla explained. "This human robot is really a robot, of course. But it looks human. Therefore, it's called a human robot."

"Yes, I'm fully aware of that," Max said. "Now, why am I here?"

"To operate on the human robot."

"I see. To take out its mechanical appendix, I suppose."

Dr. Medulla laughed. "Very funny, Doctor. But you are not here to take out. You are here to put in."

"Oh, to put *in* its mechanical appendix. Well, that ought to make medical history of some sort."

"No, Doctor, to put in the Super Boom."

"Yes, yes, now I remember," Max said. "It's all coming back. There's just one little detail that still eludes me. What *is* the Super Boom?"

"That's the explosive that you will put into the human robot," Dr. Medulla replied.

"Permanently—or just for temporary safekeeping?" Max asked, as they entered the building and proceeded along a corridor.

"That depends on the world," Dr. Medulla smiled.

"Oh."

"The Super Boom is the most destructive explosive ever developed," Dr. Medulla went on. "After you have implanted the Super Boom in the human robot, the human robot will be released. It will wander off, no one knows where. Then KAOS will announce to the world that the human robot, carrying the Super Boom, is at large."

"That'll cause some head-shaking," Max commented.

"The Super Boom can be detonated from anywhere," Dr. Medulla said. "It won't matter where the human robot roams to, we can still set off the explosive. And, if we do set off the explosive, it will destroy the whole world. But—"

"Yes?"

"But, for one hundred million dollars, we will promise *not* to detonate the explosive."

"That seems reasonable enough," Max said.

"Yes, we set the price low because, actually, we don't want to set off the explosive and destroy the whole world."

"Oh? Why not?"

Dr. Medulla lowered his voice again. "One of our junior executives has pointed out that we're part of the world," he explained. "If we blow up the world, we'll blow ourselves up, too. That's the one weak spot in our plan. Don't let it get out."

"No one will hear it from me," Max promised.

They had reached a room. Dr. Medulla opened the door, then led the party inside. On a stretcher was a human robot.

"That fellow looks familiar," Max frowned.

"Of course," Dr. Medulla smiled. "He was designed to look exactly like the average citizen. He'll look familiar to everybody. Clever, eh?"

"Very clever," Max replied. "But what's the point of it?"

"Preventive thinking," Dr. Medulla said. "When we send the human robot out into the world, then make our demand for one hundred million dollars, we are bound to make some enemies. In fact, the whole world will probably unite against us. We will be taken prisoner. We will be tortured. The world will demand to know where the human robot is, so that it can be destroyed."

"But you won't tell," Max said.

"Oh, we would gladly tell, if we were being tortured. But we won't know. So we won't be able to tell."

"Yes, but that doesn't explain why you made the robot in the image of the average man."

"Well, when the world finds out that we don't know where the human robot is, it will say, 'All right, we'll find him ourselves. Describe him.'"

"And you'll reply—"

"We'll say, 'Oh, he looks like the average man.' Among all the average-looking men in the world, let them try to find a human robot that looks like the average man!"

"By Harry, that *is* clever!" Max said.

"Are you ready to operate, Doctor?" Dr. Medulla said.

"Not quite," Max replied. "I find that an operation has a much greater chance of succeeding if I develop a personal relationship with the patient before I begin cutting."

"Oh, really? It actually helps, does it?"

"Yes. I try to get the patient to trust me before I take him to the operating room," Max said. "That way, when he has faith in me, he isn't as likely to jump up off the operating table and run out screaming when I reach for the knife."

"Hmmmm, that's interesting," Dr. Medulla said thoughtfully. "But, I think, personally, I prefer my own method."

"How do you do it?" Max asked.

"I sneak up behind them when they're not looking."

"To each his own," Max said. "Now, if you don't mind, I'd like to be alone with the patient. That is, alone with the patient, *and* my nurse."

"How long will it take?" Dr. Medulla asked.

"Oh . . . three, four days?"

"Could you trim it down to a half-hour?"

"Why not?" Max smiled. "After all, it's only the patient who has anything to lose by it."

Dr. Medulla winked. "I like your attitude, Doctor," he said, leading the other doctors out.

When Max and 99 were alone, Max quickly opened the black bag and got out an explosive. "We have a half-hour," he said. "We'll plant this pellet, then we'll climb out a window and make a run for the helicopter."

"What about me?" a mechanical-sounding voice said.

"99, I think you've caught cold," Max said.

"Max . . . that wasn't me!"

"99, think! It wasn't me. And you and I and the

human robot are the only ones in the room. So, if it wasn't you, it had to be—" He looked narrowly at the robot. "—you?"

"I was promised an operation," the robot said. "Nobody's going to cheat me out of my operation. And, incidentally, what was that business about planting a pellet?"

"Oh, that . . . that was a technical phrase," Max replied. "You wouldn't understand." He looked more closely at the human robot. "You sound almost human," he said.

"I am—half."

"Are you human enough to know what these KAOS agents intend to do to you?" Max said.

"Yes. Isn't it great!"

"Great? They intend to use you to blackmail the entire world. They'll send you out into the world, then issue an ultimatum: Put up or Blow up!"

"I'll be famous!" the human robot enthused. "I'll be on the front page of every newspaper in the world!"

"But suppose the world refuses to accept the terms? KAOS will detonate the Super Boom. You'll be destroyed."

"Big deal," the human robot replied. "Eventually, everybody dies. But how many people make the front pages?"

"Let me put it another way," Max said. "Suppose I told you that I'm not really a doctor?"

"Don't try to weasel out of a promise," the human robot said. "You can't fool me. I know you're a doctor. You're carrying a little black bag."

"All right, then suppose I told you that you don't need an operation? Suppose I told you that all you really need is a lot of rest and a lot of sunshine?"

"I'd report you to Dr. Medulla," the human robot replied.

"Oh. Well, in that case, I think I better examine you.

Sometimes an examination reveals that a patient knows more about what is best for him than the doctor. Stick out your tongue."

The human robot extended its tongue.

"Well . . . an aluminum tongue," Max commented. "That probably means something." He put an ear to the human robot's chest and listened. "Hmmmm . . . ticking. That's undoubtedly an indication of something, too. Tell me, when was the last time you ate a wristwatch?"

"Stop beating around the bush," the human robot said. "Do I get my operation or don't I?"

"Well, frankly, it's my opinion that—"

"Or do I scream for Dr. Medulla?"

"—that you are in desperate need of an operation," Max finished.

"Then let's get on with it," the human robot said. "I want to make the morning editions of the newspapers."

The door of the room opened. Dr. Medulla entered. "Time's up," he said.

"That was a fast half-hour," Max commented.

"You know how time flies in our racket," Dr. Medulla said. "It's cut, cut, cut, and, before you know it, it's dinnertime, time to carve the roast. A surgeon's work is never done. Have you established a personal relationship with the patient?"

"We detest each other," the human robot said.

"That's as it should be," Dr. Medulla replied. "What doctor wants to operate on someone he likes?" He signalled to the other doctors, who were waiting in the corridor. "Take the patient to the operating room," he said.

The other doctors entered, then wheeled away the stretcher that held the human robot.

"Everything is ready for you, Doctor," Dr. Medulla said to Max. "It is time to make history!"

"Oh?" Max said, pleased. "Do you really think it will go down in history?"

"I am certain," Dr. Medulla replied. "That is, of course, if, after the Super Boom is detonated, there is any history left."

"Max," 99 whispered. "Let's run!"

"Don't be ridiculous, 99," Max whispered back. "You heard Dr. Medulla. This may go down in history."

"But Max," 99 hissed. "If the operation is a success, and the human robot is released, and the Super Boom is detonated, you—and all of us—will die!"

"99, everybody has to die eventually," Max hissed back. "But how many people get the chance to make history?" He faced Dr. Medulla again. "When it goes down in history, what do you suppose it will be called?" he asked.

"I've taken care of that," Dr. Medulla smiled. "I've left a note, giving exact instructions. It will be known as—"

"Yes?" Max asked eagerly.

"It will be known as: Operation Operation."

"I like it," Max smiled. "It has a nice beat."

10.

WHEN MAX, 99 and Dr. Medulla reached the operating room, the patient, the human robot, was already there. He had been transferred from the stretcher to the operating table.

"If you don't mind," Max said to Dr. Medulla, "I would like to consult in private with my nurse."

"I don't mind," Dr. Medulla replied. "What does your nurse think about it?"

"Oh, I don't mind," 99 smiled. "But what do the other doctors think about it?"

"We'd better poll them," Dr. Medulla said. He addressed the other doctors, and the other nurses, who were collected around the operating table. "The motion has been made—" he began.

"I don't think that will be necessary," Max broke in. "As I recall, according to the Geneva Convention, a doctor has a right to consult with his nurse in private no matter what anyone else thinks." He signalled to 99. "Over here, nurse," he said, moving toward a secluded corner of the operating room.

When they were alone, Max said, "99, before I begin this operation, there's one question. How, exactly, do you perform an operation?"

"Max! I thought you knew!"

"Well, I have a general idea. I know you open the patient up, and sort of rummage around inside. And, too, I know you say 'scaffold' a lot. But—"

"Not 'scaffold,' Max. You say 'scalpel.' "

"Oh. Well, 'scaffold' was close. Probably no one would have noticed."

"Max, a scaffold is a temporary structure erected against a wall to support workmen. A scalpel is a knife. I think someone *might* have noticed the error."

"All right, I'll remember—scalpel, scalpel, scalpel. There now, it's etched in my mind."

"Max, are you really going through with this?" 99 said. "You don't know the first thing about surgery."

"Yes, I do," Max replied. "The first thing is: have a sharp knife. It's the second, third, fourth, fifth and so on things that I don't know the first thing about. But I have no choice, 99. We have to stall—until we can shake these KAOS people and plant the explosive."

"All right, Max. But . . . I hope you know what you're doing."

"You ought to be thankful, 99, that I don't know what I'm doing. If I knew what I was doing, I'd be so shaky I probably couldn't hold a scaffold."

"*Scalpel,* Max!"

"Oh, yes—scalpel, scalpel, scalpel. I must remember that."

"Doctor . . ." Dr. Medulla called. "The patient is ready."

Max and 99 walked to the operating table.

"Are you sure you want to go through with this?" Max said to the human robot.

The human robot turned to Dr. Medulla. "He's stalling," he said. "I demand my operation."

"Stop stalling," Dr. Medulla said to Max. "The patient demands his operation."

Max turned to a nurse. "Stop stalling," he said. "The patient demands his operation."

"What am I doing?" the nurse replied, surprised. "I'm just standing here."

"She admits it—she's stalling," Max said to Dr. Medulla.

"Stop stalling, nurse," Dr. Medulla said to the nurse. "Instead of just standing there, prepare the doctor for the operation."

The nurse popped a white cap onto Max's head. "Hold out your hands," she said.

Max extended his hands, and she slipped a pair of rubber gloves onto them. Next, she tied a mask around his face. "You're ready, Doctor," she said.

"I may be ready," Max replied, "but I feel a little silly. Do I really need these gloves and this mask?"

"They're essential," Dr. Medulla insisted.

"Are you sure? Has anybody really thought this out? Just why is it so essential that I wear a mask and rubber gloves?"

"Because, after the operation, we're all going out and rob a bank," Dr. Medulla replied. "You'll need the mask so you won't be recognized and the rubber gloves so you won't leave fingerprints on the vault."

"Fine. That's all I wanted, a logical explanation," Max said. He turned to 99. "Are my instruments ready, nurse?"

"What instruments, Max?"

"In the black bag, nurse."

"Oh. Oh, yes, Doctor."

"Is the Super Boom ready for the implant?" Max said to Dr. Medulla.

Dr. Medulla held up a small metal box. "Here it is," he said. "Cute, isn't it?"

"Cute as a mid-air collision," Max replied.

"He's stalling," the human robot complained.

"Don't rush me!" Max snapped.

"Sorry," the human robot replied. "But it's my first operation, you know."

"It's my first operation, too," Max said. "But you don't see me going all to pieces about it."

"Stop stalling," Dr. Medulla said.

"All right, here we go," Max announced. "And, as we proceed, if anyone has any suggestions to make, please speak up. This is a democratic operation. Criticism is welcome." He extended a hand toward 99. "Scaffold!" he barked.

There was silence in the operating room.

"Well, nurse," Dr. Medulla said to 99, "hand the doctor a temporary structure erected against a wall to support workers."

Max chuckled. "Oh . . . did I say 'scaffold'? I meant scalpel, nurse."

99 reached into the bag, then handed Max an instrument. It looked like a flashlight.

"Well, tough luck," Max smiled. "I guess we'll have to delay the operation until I can get my scaffold sharpened."

"That won't be necessary," Dr. Medulla said. "Use the zipper, Doctor."

"The zipper?"

"The zipper!" the human robot said disgustedly. He zipped himself open, from throat to navel, revealing his internal mechanism. "Stop stalling!"

Max stared. Inside, the human robot looked like the interior of a watch. "So, that's where that ticking was coming from," he said, relieved.

"Here's the Super Boom, Doctor," Dr. Medulla said, handing the metal box toward Max.

"Who's in charge of this operation!" Max snapped. "When I want the Super Boom, Doctor, I'll ask for it. Don't you know anything about surgery? The first rule is, before you put anything in, you first have to take something out!"

"I forgot," Dr. Medulla replied, withdrawing the Super Boom.

Max peered thoughtfully at the human robot's mechanism. "Let's see . . . what shall we take out? Something about the size of a small metal box. Ah . . . here we are—"

"Not that!" the human robot protested.

"Why not? It's the perfect size."

"That's my transistor radio," the human robot said.

"If that's your transistor radio, then I think I've found your trouble," Max said. "It's in the wrong place. Isn't it supposed to be attached to your ear?"

"It's in there so I can keep both hands free," the robot explained.

"Oh." Max inspected the mechanism again. "This may partly be the solution," he said. "If I take out this tuning fork and put in a safety pin, that will save a little space. Then if I take out . . . yes, I think this is the way to do it. I'll remove some of these larger items, and put in smaller items, and the space that is saved can be used to hold the Super Boom."

"Brilliant!" Dr. Medulla said. "I knew we had the right doctor!"

"It seems to be working out," the human robot said grudgingly. "But there for a while I thought he was stalling."

"These things take thought," Max said.

"Stop stalling!" the human robot grumbled.

Max removed a part and handed it to 99. "Something smaller," he ordered.

She handed him an item from the black bag. And Max fitted it into place.

"Can't you hurry?" the human robot complained. "It's no fun lying here with my zipper open."

"I'm operating as fast as I can," Max replied irritably.

"If you don't like the way I'm doing it, you can get up from that table and operate on yourself."

"If you don't stop stalling, I will!" the robot growled.

Max worked more quickly. The parts flew. Out of the human robot came bits and pieces of mechanism, and into the human robot went items from the black bag. Finally, Max stepped back from the table, exhausted.

"There we are," he sighed. "Now, all there is left to do is the closing." He addressed Dr. Medulla. "Would you like to zip the zipper, Doctor?"

"Haven't you forgotten something?" Dr. Medulla smiled.

"I don't think so. There seems to be plenty of room in there for the Super Boom now."

"The implant," Dr. Medulla said. "You haven't placed the Super Boom inside the human robot."

"Oh . . . that . . ."

Dr. Medulla handed the Super Boom to Max.

"Now then . . ." Max said, bending over the human robot.

At that moment, the operating room door opened.

"Shut that door!" Max cried. "Do you want to let a lot of germs in!"

"Impostor!" a voice shouted.

Max looked up. The others looked around.

In the doorway was a large man with a small black bag.

"Who are you?" Dr. Medulla asked puzzledly.

"I am the doctor!" the man replied. "I am here to perform the operation!"

"You're late," Max said. "The operation is over. But, leave your card. If another operation ever comes up, we'll call you."

"Impostor!" the man shrieked.

"If you're the doctor," Dr. Medulla said to the man, "why are you so late?"

"My car was stopped," the man replied. "There's a helicopter blocking the road."

"A likely story," Max scoffed.

"I can prove I'm the doctor," the man said. "Look—here is my little black bag!"

"But he has a little black bag, too," Dr. Medulla said, indicating Max.

"My little black bag is blacker than his little black bag!" the man raged.

Dr. Medulla looked at Max's little black bag, then at the man's little black bag. "I think you're right," he said. "Your little black bag *is* blacker than his little black bag," he said.

"Yes," Max pointed out, "but my little black bag is *littler* than his little black bag."

Dr. Medulla looked at both of the little black bags again. "That's true," he admitted. "Your little black bag *is* littler than his little black bag."

"Is somebody going to zip me up?" the human robot complained.

"Not yet," Max said. "I think I left my scaffold inside."

"Ha-hah!" the man cried. "There is the proof! He is an impostor! He doesn't know a scrample from a scaffold!"

"That did it!" Dr. Medulla shouted. He reached across the table and ripped the mask from Max's face. "You're unmasked!" he said.

"Aren't you being a little hasty?" Max protested. "How can you be sure? Maybe that other fellow is the impostor."

"No, I'm positive," Dr. Medulla replied. "The impostor is always the one who gets unmasked. And, since the other fellow isn't wearing a mask . . . well, you see how it works out."

"I'll accept that," Max replied. He turned to 99. "What was it you said earlier?"

"When, Max?"

"When we were in the examining room."

"Oh. I said, 'Let's run, Max!' "

"That's it. I knew there was a way out of this situation. All right, 99—let's run!"

Max grabbed up the black satchel and he and 99 raced from the room.

"Stop them!" the human robot cried. "I'm still unzipped!"

Max and 99 dashed down a corridor.

Behind them, they heard running, and voices crying, "Halt! Stop!"

"This is the chase," Max said to 99.

"I know, Max."

"As far as I'm concerned, it's the best part of the whole adventure," Max said. "The 'before' and the 'after' are sometimes a little dull, but the chase is always exciting."

"I feel that way about it, too, Max. I always look forward to the chase."

"I think we're coming to the part where we duck into a room and elude our pursuers," Max said.

"You're right, Max! Look! There's a door right up ahead!"

"Quick, 99! Inside!"

Max whipped open the door and he and 99 charged into the room.

"Ah! Safe!" Max breathed.

"Not yet, Max. You forgot to close the door."

"Oh . . . yes," Max said, closing the door.

They heard running outside in the corridor, and cries of "Halt! Stop!" Then the sounds passed.

"Well, it was fun while it lasted," Max said, a little disappointed.

"Max, what do we do now?" 99 asked.

"Well, first we plant the explosive. Then we slip out of the hospital unnoticed. Then we board the helicopter.

Then we return to Headquarters and receive our medals. Or, at the very least, we receive a 'job well done' from the Chief. But this time, 99, I'm *hoping* for a medal."

"Where will we plant the explosive, Max?"

Max looked around the room. "Very clever," he said. "This room is outfitted like a real hospital room. Anyone making an inspection would think that that's exactly what it was."

"What's so clever about that, Max?"

"It's clever because this isn't really a hospital. It's a place where KAOS conducts secret medical experiments. It's what I would call . . . well, a . . . a, uh . . . well, sort of a hospital. Come to think of it, I guess it isn't so clever after all."

"Max, hadn't we better hurry? Those KAOS agents will realize soon that they lost us, and they'll come back, looking for us."

"Good thinking, 99. Now, let's see where can we plant the explosive pellet?"

"In a drawer in that metal bedside table, Max?"

"No. People are always opening drawers. Especially drawers that don't belong to them."

"Under the mattress, Max?"

"No. People are always looking under mattresses. They think that's where other people hide their money."

"In that vase of flowers, Max?"

"No. The nurses are always throwing all the flowers out."

"Then, Max, I don't—"

"99! I have it. We'll plant the pellet in that water decanter!"

"But, Max—"

"It's the perfect place," Max insisted, going to the table that held the water bottle. "In a hospital, no one ever pays any attention to the water decanters. Except the patients, who are always trying to get water out of them. And, in this hospital, there are no patients."

"Maybe you're right, Max."

"Of course I am," Max said, opening the black satchel. "Now, I'll just get a pellet, and— 99 . . . where is the packet of pellets?"

"Isn't it in the bag, Max?"

"If it were in the bag, 99, would I be asking?"

"Oh, Max! You mean—"

"99, the packet is gone!"

"Oh, Max, then we've failed!"

Max sighed heavily. "Yes, 99, I'm afraid—" He suddenly brightened. "As a matter of fact, no," he smiled. "We haven't failed, 99. Our mission is completed."

"Max, what do you mean?"

"Remember the operation, 99? Remember when I was taking parts out of the human robot, and you were handing me other parts to put back in? Well, I noticed that one of the parts you handed me looked a lot like a packet of green peas. I said to myself at the time, 'I wonder why 99 is handing me this packet of green peas?' But, there was so much confusion, I didn't have the opportunity to ask you about it."

"Max, then—"

"Exactly, 99! Those pellets have been planted in the human robot!"

"Then our mission is completed, Max!"

"I think that's what I said, 99." He picked up the black satchel and he headed for the door. "Let's get out of here. I can almost feel that medal pinned on my chest already. It stings. I think the Chief pinned it right onto my skin."

"Max—wait!"

"Well, what is it, 99?" Max asked, halting.

"Our mission isn't completed, Max. Not while that human robot still exists. Max, we have a duty to the world. We have to destroy that robot."

"I don't see why, 99," Max frowned. "The Chief

didn't say anything about that when he sent us out on this mission."

"But he didn't know about the human robot, Max. If he had, I'm sure he would have told us to destroy it. Max, think! The fate of the whole world depends on our destroying not only the human robot, but the Super Boom, too."

Max smiled. "Oh, is that what you were getting at? You're worried about the Super Boom, is that it? I thought you just had it in for that robot. 99, there's no problem. The Super Boom is no longer a factor."

"But, Max, it's implanted inside the robot!"

"Of course it is. But our pellets are implanted inside the robot, too. Don't you see? 99, when we get back to Headquarters, the Chief will punch that button that's on his desk—remember? And the button will detonate the pellets. When the pellets explode, the KAOS installations will be blasted to bits. And, one of the KAOS installations is this hospital. Consequently, the Super Boom, which is planted inside the robot, which will be blasted to bits, will be destroyed in the explosion. Now, do you see?"

"I lost you, Max, back where the Chief punched the button."

"Then will you take my word for it, 99?"

"I guess I'll have to, Max. I'm sure I'd never be able to understand your explanation."

"All right, now, let's run for it, 99."

Max opened the door a crack and peeked out. "All clear," he whispered.

They slipped out of the room and moved cautiously down the corridor.

"Which way is the way out, Max?" 99 asked. "I can't remember."

"Just follow me," Max replied. "I have an unerring instinct for this sort of thing." He pointed. "See that door there? That's the way out."

"Are you sure, Max?"

"99, will you please trust my instinct," Max said, quietly opening the door. "It has never failed me—"

Max and 99 suddenly found themselves face to face with their pursuers, who were on the other side of the door, in consultation, trying to figure out which way Max and 99 had gone.

"Stop!" Dr. Medulla cried.

Max slammed the door. "Run, 99!"

Max and 99 raced down the corridor.

Behind them they heard running. Voices shouted. "Stop! Halt!"

"I think your instinct needs adjusting, Max," 99 said.

"Don't be a needler, 99," Max grumbled. "Nobody likes a needler."

11.

MAX AND 99 galloped through the hospital looking for the way out. Behind them, Dr. Medulla and the other doctors got closer and closer.

"This way!" Max shouted, opening a door.

"Max! That's the laundry!"

Max and 99 dashed off in another direction.

"Ah! This is it!" Max cried, opening another door.

"Max! That's the operating room!"

Max slammed the door, and he and 99 went racing off.

"Here it is!" Max exulted, opening another door.

"Max! That's the exit!"

Max slammed the door, and he and 99 raced away down the corridor.

As they ran, 99 said, "Max—that was the exit! Why didn't we escape?"

"The exit? I thought you said, 'Max! That's the ex—' Oh, yes, you did say it was the exit, didn't you? All right, 99, we'll run in a circle, and when we reach the exit door again, we'll use it."

Behind them, Dr. Medulla cried, "Halt! Stop!"

"I think that should be 'Stop! Halt!'" Max called back.

"Stop! Halt!"

"By George, I think he's got it!" Max said.

"Max!" 99 said, "isn't that the door? That one up ahead!"

"No, it's the next one after that," Max replied. "Trust my instinct, 99."

"All right, Max. But—"

They passed the first door. Then, reaching the second door, Max whipped it open and charged through the opening, followed by 99.

"Ah! Safe!" Max crowed.

"Max . . . we're not outside. We're . . . Max! We're in the hospital kitchen!"

"Trapped!" Max groaned.

Dr. Medulla and the other doctors appeared in the doorway.

"Trapped!" Dr. Medulla grinned.

"I just said that," Max grumbled. "However, we're both wrong. The jig is not yet up, Dr. Medulla. It just so happens that I have one more egg in my basket!"

"You don't even have a basket," Dr. Medulla pointed out.

"Will you try to be a good fellow for once in your life and go along," Max said. "Let's assume that this black bag I'm carrying is a basket."

Dr. Medulla shrugged. "I will if they will," he said, indicating the other doctors.

"Just this once," the other doctors chorused.

"All right, that's settled," Max said. He reached into the black bag, pulled out a gadget, and raised it high. "Stand back!" he commanded menacingly.

The doctors cowered against the wall.

"Don't throw it!" Dr. Medulla pleaded.

"One false move, and I drop this gadget!" Max threatened. "Now . . . clear the doorway!"

Dr. Medulla and the other doctors quickly moved away from the opening.

"Let's go, 99," Max said.

"Right behind you, Max."

They moved cautiously toward the doorway. "Let this be a lesson to you," Max said to the doctors. "A Control agent is always prepared."

"Max, what is that gadget, anyway?" 99 asked.

"I wish you hadn't asked that, 99."

"On the contrary, that's a good question," Dr. Medulla said. "What *is* that gadget, Max?"

"Run, 99!"

"Right behind you, Max!"

Max and 99 charged through the doorway, reached the corridor and raced toward the exit door.

"Max! Throw the gadget!" 99 said.

Behind them, Dr. Medulla cried, "Halt! Stop!"

"There isn't time now," Max said to 99. "Here's the door. Out!"

They dashed through the exit, out into the open air, then ran toward the gate.

"Stop! Halt!"

"Max, why don't you throw the gadget!" 99 pleaded.

"Because, 99, I haven't the vaguest idea what it is!"

"Then why did you threaten those KAOS agents with it? And why did they cower against the wall?"

"Instinct, 99. Whenever rival groups of agents meet face to face, one agent in one group always pulls a gadget from a little black bag and cries, 'Stand back!' And the other group of agents always stands back, cowering against the wall. It's tradition."

"I'm sorry I asked that question and spoiled things, Max."

"You're forgiven, 99. Just run!"

They were reaching the gate.

"Stop! Halt!" the sentry cried, barring the way.

"We can't!" Max called. "We're being pursued!"

"You're supposed to show your identification!" the sentry bawled.

"We'll show our identification twice the next time!" Max promised.

"You won't forget?"

"Scout's honor!"

The sentry stepped aside, and Max and 99 went racing through the gateway.

"Stop! Halt!" they heard the sentry cry, behind them, as the doctor approached the gate.

"Halt! Stop!" Dr. Medulla answered.

"That's my line!" the sentry raged.

Max and 99 sprinted onward. Ahead they saw the helicopter waiting for them. Behind them they heard a shot. A bullet zinged by.

"Now there's a bunch of poor losers for you!" Max said disgustedly.

They reached the helicopter and leaped aboard. "Up!" Max commanded Lance Chalfont.

Lance Chalfont looked disturbed. "Up. Is that that way?" he said, pointing upward, "Or that way?" he asked, pointing downward. "I always get the two mixed up."

A bullet whizzed by the plane.

"Never mind! I think I remember!" Lance Chalfont said, jumping into the pilot's seat and grabbing the controls.

A moment later, the helicopter whirred upward.

A hail of bullets flew at the plane.

"They got us!" Lance Chalfont cried.

"Where?"

"In the left coconut!" Lance Chalfont replied.

"Is it bad?"

"Terrible!" Lance Chalfont replied. "When we get

back to civilization, we'll have to operate to get that bullet out of the coconut."

"But can we fly?" Max asked.

Lance Chalfont smiled. "I don't think we can," he replied. "But, there ain't no need for us to fly, anyway. The helicopter can do it for us."

"That's what I meant," Max said. "Can the heli—oh, never mind." He turned to 99. "Are you all right, 99?"

"Fine, Max."

Max dropped into his seat, relaxed and smiled. "Mission accomplished," he said. "Lance, you can fly us back to Headquarters now. There is an explosive planted in each of the several KAOS installations. And, it's button-pushing time!"

"Max! We've done it!" 99 cried happily.

"Yesss . . . we were rather magnificent, weren't we? I don't see how we can miss getting medals for this, 99." He opened the black bag and started to drop the gadget into it, then paused. "I wonder what this thing really is?" he said curious.

"Read the instructions, Max."

Max read. " 'When trapped by group of KAOS agents, raise gadget high over head and order KAOS agents to Stand Back. KAOS agents will automatically comply. It is traditional that all secret agents cower against wall when cry of Stand Back is issued. Note: If occasion does not arise where you are trapped, gadget can also be used to supply between-meal snack. It is filled with jelly beans.' "

"R & D is thoughtful," 99 commented.

Max opened the gadget, then extended it toward 99. "Jelly bean?"

"Thank you, Max," 99 replied, taking one.

"Lance?" Max said.

"Never between meals," Lance Chalfont replied. "I got to keep my figure. Ain't nothin' worse for the image than seein' a fat, sloppy silent birdman."

"Max, shouldn't you contact the Chief?" 99 said.
"Good thinking, 99."
Max took off his shoe and dialed.

Operator: About time! Where've you been with our shoe, Max?

Max: Completing the mission, Operator. Now, may I speak to the Chief, please?

Operator: Not with those jelly beans in your mouth. It's not polite.

Max: Sorry about that, Operator. (sound of swallowing) Now, Operator?

Operator: I will ring your number, sir.

Chief: Is that you, Max?

Max: Yes, Chief, this is Max (He Did It Again) Smart reporting. I guess I don't have to tell you how the mission came out.

Chief: Max, you mean you bungled again?

Max (a little hurt): Is that fair, Chief? When did I ever bungle?

Chief: Do you want me to read you the list from the top down, Max, or from the bottom up?

Max: Neither will be necessary, Chief. Anyway, in spite of anything that may have happened before, this time I have been completely successful. A pellet has been planted in every KAOS installation. In other words, Chief, you can now punch the button.

Chief: Not quite yet, Max.

Max: Oh? Why not, Chief? Sore finger?

Chief: No, that's not it, Max. Frankly, I'd rather not discuss the reason.

Max: Is it because— Chief! That KAOS agent who was planting explosives in the Control installations— was he successful, too?

Chief: Yes, Max. That's one of the reasons. Now, Max, I want you and 99 to hurry right back here to Headquarters.

Max: Is something up, Chief?

Chief: Yes, Max, something definitely is up.

Max: Can't you tell me what it is? Can't you even give me a hint?

Chief: I'd rather not, Max. This line may be bugged.

Operator: I resent that! If you're talking about me, I haven't heard a word you said! Do you think I have nothing more important to do than sit around listening to a couple of kooks?

Chief: I didn't mean you, Operator.

Operator: I should hope not! Incidentally, what *is* up, Chief?

Chief: Sorry, Operator. It's Top Top Secret.

Max: Yes, Operator, it's Top Top Secret. But, because you're such a nice operator, I'll see that you get an invitation to the ceremony.

Operator: Ceremony?

Chief: Ceremony?

Max: You don't really have to keep it a Top Top Secret, Chief. I have a pretty good idea what it is. Tell me, is it a round medal or a square medal?

Chief: I haven't the thinnest notion what you're talking about, Max. But it isn't important. Just get back here as quickly as possible.

Max: I get it, Chief. You want it to be a surprise. Well, don't worry. I promise that I'll look surprised.

Chief (wearily): You do that, Max. I'll see you both later.

Max: So long, Chief.

Operator: So long from me, too, Chief. And, Max—

Max: Yes, Operator?

Operator: Congratulations. About the medal, I mean. If anybody deserves it, you do. Max . . . could I ask a favor?

Max: Anything, Operator.

Operator: Max, when you get the medal . . . will you wear it on your shoe?

Max: On my *shoe,* Operator?

Operator: We'd be so proud, here at the telephone company.

Max: I'm afraid not, Operator. That would be a little obvious. A KAOS agent would see it and know instantly that I was a Control agent.

Operator: How about *in* your shoe, then?

Max: Sorry again, Operator. Too obvious. The KAOS agents would soon learn that Max Smart was the Control agent who limped.

Operator: Max, if you won't wear it *on* your shoe, or *in* your shoe, I have another suggestion.

Max: Goodbye, Operator.

Max hung up.

"What did he say, Max?" 99 asked.

"Top Top Secret, 99." He turned to Lance Chalfont. "Back to home base," he said. "The Chief wants us at Headquarters as soon as we can get there."

Lance Chalfont frowned. "Home base . . . is that up or down?"

"Straight east," Max replied. "That's 'E' on the compass."

"Well, ding-dong, is *that* what that means? I thought that 'E' was for 'Enywhere.' "

As the helicopter buzzed off toward the East Coast, 99 questioned Max again. "Can't you tell *me,* Max? I'm one of the gang."

"I don't think I should, 99. The Chief wouldn't admit what it really is. He wants us to be surprised. But I will give you a hint—it's something that you couldn't conveniently wear on your shoe."

"Max! A medal!"

"Drat! You guessed it!"

Not long after that, the helicopter settled down at the airport in Washington. Max and 99 said goodbye to Lance Chalfont, then got into Max's car and drove toward Control headquarters.

"We ought to work on our acceptance speeches," Max said.

"But, Max, if we had an acceptance speech, the Chief would know that we weren't surprised."

"I don't mean a formal acceptance speech," Max replied. "I mean something off the top of the head. How's this for a beginning? 'A funny thing happened to me on my way here to receive this medal.' "

"That might give it away, Max. Why don't you leave out the part 'to receive this medal'?"

"All right. 'A funny thing happened to me on my way here.' "

"You better leave out 'on my way here,' Max. Why else, at this particular time, would you be heading toward 'here' if not to receive a medal?"

"I'll go along with that, 99. 'A funny thing happened to me.' "

"Max, every speech begins that way. The Chief will know it's a speech. Cut out 'A funny thing happened to me.' "

"99, that leaves me with nothing."

"Max, that's it! The perfect length for an off-the-top-of-the-head acceptance speech."

Max smiled. "I rather like it too," he said.

A few minutes later they pulled up in front of Control Headquarters. They entered and hurried to the Chief's office. Max knocked on the door.

"What state is round on both ends and high in the middle?" a voice replied.

"Is that the password, Chief?" Max called in.

"Yes, Max."

Max thought for a moment. "Pennsylvania? It has mountains in the middle."

"No, Max," the Chief replied. "Ohio."

"Oh. Ohio, Chief."

"Come in, Max."

Max and 99 entered the Chief's office. The Chief was seated at his desk, looking somewhat concerned.

"You can pin it right here, Chief," Max smiled, offering the lapel of his jacket.

"Max, I don't have time to play games," the Chief said sharply. "We're in a state of tension here."

"I thought you said the state was Ohio." He looked thoughtful again. "Tension? How many states over is that from the state that looks like a poodle, Chief?"

"I don't think that's what the Chief means, Max," 99 said.

"Oh?" He turned to the Chief. "What do you mean then, Chief?"

"Max, KAOS and Control have reached an impasse," the Chief replied. "The race turned out to be a tie. There are now explosives planted in both the Control installations and the KAOS installations."

"Then quick—the button!" Max urged.

"No, Max, we have to wait. A conference is in progress. The top men in Control, and in KAOS, are now in a meeting . . . with Him."

"With Him!"

"Yes, Max, with Him!"

"This *is* big stuff!" Max said. "What's the meeting about, Chief?"

"Well, Max, since KAOS and Control both have the means to destroy each other, it seems that both are in danger of being destroyed."

"That adds up," Max nodded.

"Consequently," the Chief went on, "Him called a meeting of the top brass of both organizations and asked them to reason together. That's what they're doing right now."

"You mean, Chief, they're trying to think of a reason why they should destroy each other?"

"No, Max, a reason why they *shouldn't* destroy each other."

"If that's all they need, I can give them a reason. It's messy. That's always an excellent reason."

"I'll remember that, in case Him calls and asks for suggestions," the Chief replied.

"Chief, as long as we're just sitting around waiting, can't we get on with the ceremony?" Max said.

"Ceremony, Max?"

"The you-know-what. The surprise."

"I don't know what you're talking about, Max."

"The m-e-d-a-l-s, Chief."

"Max, make sense. Metal what?"

"Not metal! Medal! 99 and I are supposed to receive medals for successfully carrying out the mission."

"I don't know anything about it," the Chief said gruffly.

"You don't?"

"No. I don't have any medals for you, Max."

"Well . . . I guess *that's* the surprise," Max said disappointedly.

The telephone rang. The Chief picked up the receiver. "Chief here," he said. Then, getting a response, he jumped to his feet and snapped to attention.

"It's Him!" Max said to 99.

"Yes, sir," the Chief said into the phone. "Yes, sir, that is, that's wonderful news! Thank you for calling, sir." He hung up.

"What is it, Chief?" 99 said excitedly.

"Wonderful news!" the Chief beamed.

"We know that," Max said. "But what is the news?"

"Max . . . 99 . . . KAOS and Control have declared Peace!"

"Wonderful!" 99 cried.

Max looked glum. "I don't see what's so wonderful about it," he said. "Don't you realize what this means? We're all out of a job."

"On the contrary, Max," the Chief said. "In fact, we'll be busier than ever. We'll have to hire more agents."

"I don't quite follow that, Chief," Max said.

"Don't you see? We're at peace, yes. But, to make sure that we remain at peace, we'll both have to make sure that the other fellow doesn't cheat. That means we'll have to hire lots more spies to keep an eye on the KAOS organization. And, of course, the KAOS people will have to hire a lot more spies to keep an eye on us. Him was very happy about that part of it. Him is in favor of anything that increases employment."

"Wonderful!" Max cried excitedly. "Hooray for Him!"

"Yes, it's a great day, Max," the Chief said. "Just think—Control and KAOS at peace!"

"Yes, a great day," Max agreed. "And, I think 99 and I can take part of the credit for it. After all, if we hadn't planted those pellets that made it possible for Control to destroy KAOS completely, there wouldn't be any Peace. We did a top-notch job. I wouldn't be surprised if somebody decided to award us medals."

"I wouldn't count on it, Max," the Chief said.

"Oh, well, the medal isn't important," Max said. "What is important is the sense of satisfaction one gets from knowing that he was responsible for the cessation of hostilities between two warring organizations."

"Max, you didn't do it *all* by yourself, you know."

"I realize that," Max replied, ambling toward the Chief's desk. "Him played his little part, too. But, in the final analysis, I think it can be said—" Max sat down on the corner of the Chief's desk. "—that—"

The whole room suddenly trembled.

"Hmmm . . . must be an earthquake somewhere," Max said.

"Max!" the Chief cried, horror-stricken.

"Yes, Chief?"

"Max! You sat on the button!"

Max got up off the corner of the desk. He looked where he had been sitting. He winced. "Sorry about that, Chief," he murmured.

The phone rang, and the Chief snatched up the receiver. "Chief here," he said dimly. Then he jumped to his feet and snapped to attention.

"It's Him," Max whispered to 99. "He must have a P.S."

"Yes, sir," the Chief said into the phone. "Yes, sir, I know, sir. Yes, sir, I'm sorry about that, sir. Yes, sir, I'm sorry about that, too, sir. Yes, sir, I will, sir, yes, sir." He hung up, then faced Max.

"Did you, uh, tell him that somebody accidentally sat on the button, Chief?" Max asked.

"He already knew it, Max," the Chief replied coldly.

"Oh. Well, as they say, bad news travels fast."

"Max, everything that was done, you have undone. You have destroyed the KAOS installations!"

"In that case, I think we better get set for an explosion. Now it's KAOS's turn."

"No, we don't have to worry about that," the Chief said. "KAOS's own button was located at one of those installations. You destroyed it."

"Oh. Well, then, Chief, what did I do wrong?"

"You also destroyed every chance for a lasting Peace. The KAOS brass was outraged when you blew up their installations."

"I hate to say this about an ex-enemy, Chief," Max replied. "But those KAOS people always were a bunch of soreheads."

"They're not ex-enemies any more, Max."

"You mean?"

"I mean that war has been re-declared. The KAOS people swear to rebuild their installations, regroup their forces, and resume the conflict."

"Plucky, aren't they?" Max frowned.

The Chief dropped into his chair. He held his head in his hands. "Max! How could you have done it!" he groaned.

Max shrugged. "It could have happened to anybody, Chief."

"Max! You . . . you . . . you . . . words fail me!"

Max suddenly brightened. "Chief, I'll tell you what. To make up for it—"

"Yes, Max?" the Chief said, raising his head, looking at Max hopefully.

"You can forget about the medal," Max said graciously.

GET SMART!

by William Johnston

When Max Smart, that intrepid secret agent for Control, gets assigned to the Computer Caper, it's the start of a laugh-out-loud adventure through a confusing labyrinth of international spies, UN delegates, Greenwich Village coffee house denizens, and a couple of beautiful girls who don't do much to help him but do liven up the nutty goings-on.

How Max foils the fiendish plot against the Free World makes a zany tale that no self-respecting spy lover can afford to miss.

T-103   A TEMPO BOOK   60¢

SORRY, CHIEF...

by William Johnston

When the diabolical Dr. X invents a serum capable of making man invisible and threatens to sell it to KAOS, the fate of the whole world hangs in the balance.

Only one man can jump into the breach against the Forces of Evil—Maxwell Smart, Agent 86 from Control. Max's assignment: to apprehend Dr. X, get the serum and formula, and, most important, bring back alive the six invisible guinea pigs, proof that the serum works.

Does Max succeed in his quest? Does the whole civilized world triumph? Would you believe it?

T-119   A Tempo Book   60¢

GET SMART
ONCE AGAIN!

by William Johnston

Never before has Maxwell Smart been involved in such a vast panorama of intrigue.

With Peaches Twelvetrees, the beautiful blonde cryptographer, to aid him, Max sets forth for New York, Moscow, and Peking, desperately trying to find the key to the Dooms Day Plan while eluding KAOS's master spy, I. M. Noman, whose India rubber face allows him to change his appearance at will.

Will KAOS snatch back the beautifully intricate code before its dread secret is revealed? Or will Max, once again, outSmart his enemies and save humanity? The Free World awaits the answer.

T-121   A TEMPO BOOK   60¢

If you enjoyed this book, you will want to read these other absorbing TEMPO BOOKS.

LT. ROBIN CRUSOE, U.S.N., by Bill Ford. T138 50¢
Rib-tickling tale of a modern Crusoe who needs all his ingenuity to keep from going native—or nuts!

THE PUSHCART WAR, by Jean Merrill. T104 50¢
The historical (hysterical) story of New York's Pushcart War of 1976 . . . including the Daffodil Massacre and the Pea Shooter Campaign.

THREE MEN ON THIRD, by Gene Olson. T126 50¢
When a wacky team has a coach who doesn't know a home run from a hypotenuse, the ball game is strictly for laughs.

WILD WHEELS, by Carl H. Rathjen. Introduction by Stirling Moss. Roy Hammond decides that auto racing is the life for him. T97 50¢

PENROD, by Booth Tarkington. The side-splitting story about the Worst Boy in Town. T72 50¢

PETER PAN, by James M. Barrie. The classic story of Peter and Wendy and the amazing adventures that befall them in Never-Never-Land. T95 50¢

ARE WE ALL HERE? by Oren Arnold. A hilarious account of a rollicking Continental tour. T53 50¢

THE GNOMOBILE, by Upton Sinclair. The merry, madcap adventures of Elizabeth and Rodney and two delightful gnomes in search of a home. T112 50¢

HIGH ROAD HOME, by William Corbin. Evading pursuers, living by his wits, Nico set forth across the vast American continent in search of his father. T29 50¢

THE RED CAR, by Don Stanford. Thrills and excitement as Hap Adams rebuilds his beat-up MG for the big race. T10 50¢

ROOSEVELT GRADY, by Louisa R. Shotwell. Roosevelt dreamed of living in one place where he would not be an outsider, but for a migrant worker's family, this wasn't easy. T67 50¢

SCREWBALL, by Alberta Armer. Mike longed for something he could do as well as his twin—then he discovered the exciting world of racing cars. T74 50¢

GIANTS UNLEASHED, by Groff Conklin. The infinite power of intelligence in the Universe explored in twelve unforgettable Science Fiction stories. T111 50¢

FURY: STALLION OF BROKEN WHEEL RANCH, by Albert G. Miller. A heartwarming story which introduces Fury, the renowned horse of television. T14 50¢

OFF THE BEAM, by James L. Summers. The hilarious misadventures of a high-school junior and his far-out friends. T19 50¢

THE STORY OF WINSTON CHURCHILL, by   T85   50¢
Alida Sims Malkus. The life and times
of the most remarkable man of this cen-
tury, movingly told for the post-war gen-
eration.

THE STORY CATCHER, by Mari Sandoz.   T90   50¢
The moving story of how an Indian boy
proved himself a man in the eyes of his
people.

ROD SERLING'S THE TWILIGHT ZONE.   T89   50¢
Weird tales of bizarre events too strange
to be believed, yet too grippingly real to
be doubted.

SEA FEVER, by K. M. Peyton. When Matt   T76   50¢
lost his father to the cruel sea, he gained
an enemy who would not cease his pur-
suit as long as Matt knew the hideous
truth.

ACROSS FIVE APRILS, by Irene Hunt.   T98   50¢
Young Jethro was forced to leave his
boyhood behind during the five fateful
years of the Civil War.

THE UNITED STATES IN WORLD WAR II,   T69   50¢
by Don Lawson. A comprehensive, fac-
tual history from Pearl Harbor to VE
and VJ days.

If your dealer does not have the books you want,
ORDER from **TEMPO BOOKS,** 51 Madison Avenue, New
York, N.Y. 10010 enclosing check or money order—
no currency or C.O.D.'s, please. Please include 10¢ per
book for postage and handling. A complete list of titles
is available upon request.